Midni
Rider
FOR THE MORNING STAR

from the life and times of
Francis Asbury

francis asbury press

Francis Asbury Press
publishes significant
scholarly, educational,
and popular books to
promote a Wesleyan
understanding of the
Christian faith.

Midnight Rider

FOR THE MORNING STAR

from the life and times of Francis Asbury

Mark Alan Leslie

francis asbury press

Scripture quotations are from The New King James Version, except in the Epilogue, where The New American Standard Version is quoted.

Editor: Harold W. Burgess
Designer: Vicki New
Cover: Mark Alan and Loy Leslie
Cover Photograph: by Sherwood Burton of Daystar Images
Cover Painting: by Harry Cochrane. The painting is located in the United Church of Monmouth, Maine. Permission to reproduce the image was given by the Executive Board of the church.

ISBN 978-0-915143-10-8

For Information contact

Francis Asbury Press
P.O. Box 7
Wilmore, KY 40390
859-858-4222
E-mail: francisasb@aol.com
Website: www.francisasburysociety.com

Francis Asbury Press is an imprint of The Francis Asbury Society, Inc.

I dedicate this book to the One who guided
my hands in writing it, the Holy Spirit,
through and by my Lord and Savior,
Jesus Christ.

CONTENTS

ACKNOWLEDGEMENTS

I want to thank my wife, Loy, for her undeterred faith in God and in my writing and for putting up with the sometimes odd hours I have done so — as well as for her help in researching Francis Asbury's life. Thanks, also, to Harold Burgess of The Francis Asbury Society and all those at the Society's headquarters who helped bring this project to fruition. I am indebted to my good friend and photographer Sherwood Burton (www.daystarimages.com) for his photograph of the painting of Bishop Asbury that hangs in the United Church of Monmouth. A special thank-you is extended to the congregation of that church for the use of that image.

I am indebted to my editors, Bob Wood and Joyce Thomas, for their input.

During our research about Asbury, my wife and I found particular help from *A Methodist Saint: The Life of Bishop Asbury*, written in 1927 by Herbert Asbury; *The Pioneer Bishop: The Life and Times of Francis Asbury*, written in 1858 by W.P. Strickland; *Francis Asbury: The Prophet of the Long Road*, written by Ezra Squier Tipple; and Asbury's journals. But I give special thanks to Darius L. Salter, pastor of Richardson (Texas) Church of the Nazarene and past professor of Christian Preaching and Pastoral Theology at Nazarene Theological Seminary in Kansas City, Missouri, author of *America's Bishop: The Life of Francis Asbury*.

Of course, to God be all the glory!

FOREWORD

The Harry Cochrane painting of the dashing Francis Asbury atop a gray stallion, crossing a creek in the wilderness, grabbed my attention the first time I attended United Church of Monmouth in Maine.

This older gentleman, his cape flying behind, holding what appeared to be a Bible in one hand while his other held the reins along with a hat, demanded attention. Well, he got mine, but not fully for a number of years while I was busy with other writing projects.

Finally, when my wife, Loy, and I seriously began researching Asbury's life, we were astounded by several things: his zeal, tenaciousness, perseverance, daring, uncommon faith, determination, and ability to bring hardened sinners of the worst kind to their knees before their Savior.

All of this came together in this extraordinary man of God—a man who could swap war story for war story with the apostle Paul.

Indeed, Asbury was chased by Indians, hunted by savage wolves, shot at by highwaymen, hid in a swamp for three days while soldiers searched for him, bruised by saplings, bitten by mosquitoes and drenched with malaria vapors, escaped the ravages of yellow fever, and pelted by hailstones of such size that "three of them filled a pint measure."

The title, *Midnight Rider for the Morning Star*, depicts the life of Asbury, who often rode through the night and with one purpose: to spread the word about the Morning Star—Jesus. As Peter wrote in II Peter 1:19: "And we have the word of the prophets made more certain, and you will do well to pay attention to it, as to a light shining in a dark place, until the day dawns and the morning star rises in your hearts." And as the Lord said in Revelations 22:16: "I, Jesus, have sent my angel to give you this testimony for the churches. I am the Root and the Offspring of David, and the bright Morning Star."

During our exploration and writing, the Holy Spirit has opened my eyes. He has taken me from the heights of exhilaration over this man's amazing life and accomplishments to the depths of many uneasy moments when considering the extent my own "spirituality."

Asbury's story is certainly one that should push every one of us to strive to do better and to be better.

It reminds me of a poem I wrote, entitled Sold Out or a Hold-out? It reads like this:

> *Are you sold out*
> *Or a hold-out?*
> *Do you mean it when you call Me Lord?*
>
> *Do you put Me first,*
> *Do you really thirst*
> *For every last morsel of My Word?*
>
> *How much do you care,*
> *How much do you dare*
> *To speak boldly in proclaiming My Name?*
>
> *Put Me first in your heart,*
> *With My love each day start*
> *If the title "Christian" you claim.*
>
> *Are you sold out*
> *Or a hold-out?*
> *Zealous for God*
> *And jealous of your time with Me?*
>
> *Be sold out,*
> *Not a hold-out.*
> *I'll give you strength, says the Lord,*
> *And set you free.*

John Wesley urged his followers to "do all the good you can, by all the means you can, in all the ways you can, in all the places you can, at all the times you can, to all the people you can, as long as you ever can."

That was good advice then. It's grand advice today.

Mark Alan Leslie
30 Ridge Road
Monmouth, ME 04259
gripfast@roadrunner.com

CHAPTER 1

A Race for Life and Limb

The air was so clear and crisp on this autumn day that it almost crackled. The aroma of salt from the nearby Atlantic Ocean mingled with the scent of the balsam fir trees all about him to create a curious combination. And the trees were so startlingly beautiful, adorned in brilliant yellows, reds and oranges, that they nearly whistled, "Look at us!" But neither the air, the aroma nor the foliage attracted the attention of the man on the tall, gray stallion. With one hand controlling the reins, the other cradling a book, and comfortably settled into his saddle, he was engrossed in the odd-looking characters that read right to left.

"*Ani la dodi va dodi le*," he read aloud. "I am of my beloved and my beloved is of me...." He thought for a moment. "Ah, 'I am my beloved's and my beloved is mine.' Oh, I love that scripture!"

Francis Asbury turned to his companion, then remembered that Nicholas wasn't with him at the moment but had ridden on ahead to make arrangements for the week's meetings.

I wish I had grown up speaking Hebrew and had to learn English rather than the other way around, he thought absent-mindedly with a chuckle. But he had taught himself Hebrew just as he had taught himself Greek, and he guessed he was better off for that than if he had spent four years at university learning the languages. That would have delayed his ministry and shortened his time to save men's lives. *So university may have been a sin in the end, eh? Silly thought.*

Suddenly the hair on the back of his neck rose.

Something dark, something sinister lurked nearby. He pulled himself upright in his saddle, quietly shut his book and slowly scanned the woods around him, listening intently. Somewhere to his left squirrels began squawking loudly and agitatedly and something large, a partridge perhaps, battered wings through the underbrush in a rush skyward.

Something menacing. He couldn't see anything physically, but he sensed it spiritually. Something ominous nearby.

Francis tucked the Hebrew Torah into his shirt, bent down to his horse's ear, whispered, "Come on, Spark. Cha!" and the big stallion responded with a thrust that sent his rider back into the rear of the saddle.

Suddenly a shot rang out from the woods to his left and Asbury heard a bullet hiss past. He lowered his head, bent toward the horse's neck and kicked his heels into the stallion's ribs, urging loudly now, "Hurry, boy. Hurry! Cha!"

An excellent horseman, Asbury had ridden more than two hundred thousand miles from Georgia to Quebec, up and down the Atlantic seaboard over the previous thirty-eight years. But he would need more than skill on his horse today. Even Spark couldn't outrun a bullet.

He lifted a prayer toward the heavens. "Lord, quicken our step."

The path was barely two yards wide, an old Indian trail not wide enough for a carriage or wagon to pass—a shortcut he had used before. Francis turned to look behind him. Dark silhouettes on horseback rode in chase, probably a hundred yards away, visible only in the shafts of light flickering between the shadows of the trees. Two, maybe three that he could see. No. There was a fourth, to his left—probably the one who had fired the shot.

Francis turned to look forward. A branch! He ducked just in time, and reached to catch hold of his hat as the limb nearly snapped it off his head. Spark, sure-footed through years of riding narrow trails in the dark of night, avoiding roots that stuck out of the ground, shouldered around a turn in the path as if he knew to tighten the turns to shorten the distance he must run.

Behind them, men were shouting directions to one another. Cursing. Other, muffled words he could not understand. Did these men know of a shortcut, through a field perhaps, to get in front of him?

"Lord, guide our path!" Francis called, thinking his creaking joints were too aged for a dash through the thick woods.

As he rode on, his senses heightened. He heard the sound of the leather saddle creaking beneath him, felt the lungs of his horse expand and contract, smelled the sweat that glistened on the great stallion's neck. He looked for a landmark. He had been so absorbed in his reading that he hadn't known precisely where he was. He must be somewhere approaching Scarborough—near the meeting hall at Massacre Pond, where most of the local townspeople had been slaughtered by hostile Indians more than one hundred years before, back in the 1690s. The salt marshes and ocean would be somewhere, not far, eastward to his right.

Another shot rang out, and another, one bullet snapping through a branch just a yard or two to Francis' right. A shiver of fright flew down his spine.

"Giddya!" he hollered, and Spark seemed to stretch out his stride and drop lower to the ground. Francis pulled his hat down to his ears. Yes, he knew this path! There was Dunstan's Brook up ahead. Putting his right hand to Spark's neck, he spoke into his ear, "Don't slow down at the water, boy. Fire right through it!"

As if understanding every word, the horse leaped into the fifteen-yard-wide stream, causing Francis to hold on for dear life as he plowed fiercely through the quickly flowing water. Asbury prayed that they would get to the other side before the highwaymen reached it. If not, he was a dead man.

Another shot sounded and a bullet hit the water beside him with a muffled thud.

"Too many souls still to reach, Lord!" he called out. "Protect Your child!"

A verse from a Psalm flashed before him—"*May the Lord fulfill your purpose*"—and he called again to the heavens, "Lord, my purpose isn't fulfilled yet!"

Suddenly, as if sprung from a jack-in-the-box, Spark and Francis bounded out of the stream. Springing to the top of the four-foot-high stream bank, Spark bent into a turn in the path, entering a thick grove of balsam fur trees. Francis knew he was only a quarter of a mile or so from the village at that point. He heard loud cursing behind him; the rogues must have reached the stream.

Then, from his right another gunshot rang out. This time the bullet crackled through branches overhead. *The rifle sights must be off,* Francis thought with a strained smile. He lay prostrate along Spark's back and settled his head to the left of the horse's grand neck.

Francis refrained from digging in his heels. He and his horse were of one mind. He was sure of that. Speed to safety. Speed. Safety. His senses now fully awakened, he didn't feel his sixty-four years of age at all. He simply felt he had to hang on now.

A moment later, they dashed out of the woods and into an open field that led into the village of Scarborough some two hundred yards away. Surging toward the town, he leaned down to Spark's ear and cooed, "You're the best, Spark. I've loved all my horses, but you're the brightest and the best." Thinking of the close call he had just escaped, he laughed and added aloud, "And the fastest."

As he approached the guardpost, he waved up to Horatio Short, who hollered down to him, "I heard gunfire, Bishop Asbury. Are you all right?"

"By the grace of God and the skin of my teeth, Horatio. Keep your eye out for trouble, though."

"Your sidekick's in the general store, Bishop."

Francis nodded, slowed Spark and guided him to the right, down what had become the village main street. How these people had bravely moved here in spite of the Indian slaughter was almost astonishing. They had courageous hearts, many of which he, Jesse Lee, or Bishop Philip Wagner had won to Christ.

Pulling Spark to a stop at the store, Francis dismounted, threw the reins over the hitching post, pulled the Hebrew Torah from inside his shirt and stuffed it into his saddlebag.

"Bishop Asbury! Bishop Asbury!" He looked up to see a small boy running toward him.

"Thomas!" he acknowledged the youth with a laugh.

The boy rushed up to him and held up his arms. Asbury bent to pick him up—a good-sized child of seven years. Raised up in the man's grasp, Thomas hugged him as best he could with his little arms.

Francis looked lovingly at the boy. "Have you been minding your P's and Q's?"

Thomas nodded. "Yessir!"

"He's been so looking forward to your visit, Bishop." The lilting voice of Abigail Brackett reached Francis' ears and he noticed the beautiful woman approach. Abigail was dressed in the earthy, functional dress of a pioneer woman, but it didn't conceal that she was as stately as a lady-in-waiting in the Queen's court.

"He wanted his face washed and trousers clean for your arrival," she added with a smile as she continued on toward him. A basket hung in the crook of her arm. "He said he knew you'd want to cuddle him up."

A tear trickled down Francis' cheek at the thought of the boy's love, and, vaguely, of the children he himself had never had.

He squeezed the child. "Well, Thomas," he said, catching the boy's eyes firmly in his own, "you certainly are cleaner than this dirty traveler before you!"

Thomas smiled proudly, then something grabbed his attention as he looked at Francis' hat. His brow knit into a question mark.

"You've got a hole in your hat," the boy declared.

"A hole?"

Thomas raised a finger to Francis' hat and poked it into a hole the size of a pencil. "Hey, it goes right straight through!" he squealed.

"What?" Francis set the boy on his feet and removed his hat.

Sure enough. There were matching holes on either side of his hat. Francis pondered the mystery, but just for a moment.

"That last bullet," he said quietly.

•••••

Three hours later, after a meal of lamb chops, potatoes and green beans, Francis sat contentedly in the great room of the impressive cottage of Sam and Abigail Brackett—a two-story home rare in this wilderness. Abigail had just refreshed everyone's cup of tea, and Francis held the hot mug in his hands.

"I'm so sorry I wasn't there with you this afternoon," Nicholas Snethen said.

Francis studied his young companion. Worried about Asbury's health after battles with an ulcerated throat and with the pleurisy and rheumatism from the repeated drenchings and cold winds that laced him in his travels, the Methodist Conference had commissioned Nicholas to be Francis' travel companion, both as an attendant and co-ambassador to America. In three days he and Nicholas would ride north to the New England Conference in Monmouth, where they would be joined by another companion, Henry Boehm.

Here it was, 1809, nearly four decades after he had arrived in the colonies, and *now* they were worried about his health. Ha! They didn't know the half of the story—the dangers he had faced, the escapes he had made.

He looked again at his companion, taking stock of whom he considered a fine young man. Francis had grown to love Nicholas as dearly as he did Jesse Lee, who had first brought Christ to this northern wilderness. And, through Francis' tutelage, Nicholas was becoming more and more versed in the Word of God. But, honestly, if Nicholas had been with him this afternoon, it might have been disastrous. A preacher, he was. A horseman, he was not.

Francis smiled at his young friend. "Your presence, son, would have meant the necessity of calling one more angel into duty to protect us."

Everyone laughed, including little Thomas who sat at Francis' feet. Nicholas playfully biffed him on the head.

"Well, Francis, you're with us tonight, and for that we're

thankful." It was Sam Brackett, a tall, burly man in his mid-30s who owned this cabin in the Province of Maine in the Commonwealth of Massachusetts.

Sam and Abigail knew Francis well. He had stayed at their home on his circuit-ride to the Commonwealth every couple of years for a decade now. They were honored by his presence. The best-recognized man in America—more so than George Washington—everywhere Francis went crowds gathered to hear him preach.

And why not? Sam thought as he gazed upon his friend, whose long white locks flowed to the neck of his shirt. For all his sicknesses and ills, Francis had aged well, maintaining his ruggedly handsome features and commanding presence. His black clothes were a model of neatness and plainness that added to his air of dignity and venerable appearance. He seemed to stand much taller than his five-foot-nine height. He possessed broad shoulders, a square jaw, piercing blue eyes, a prominent nose and a large mouth, as if purposely made to preach life to the dead.

And preach, he did. Francis had grown the Methodist Episcopal Church from six hundred members to more than two hundred thousand, had ordained four thousand preachers, had presided over more than two hundred annual Conference sessions, had brought men and women to tears of repentance in thousands of sermons. In his presence, people knew they were hearing words from the throne room of God.

Sam himself had seen grown men—hunters and trappers—fall under the anointed preaching of this man, some as if they were truly dead; others, hardened men even, weeping like schoolchildren as the hound of heaven gave their souls chase.

"Will you tell me the wolf story again, Bishop?" Thomas was absent-mindedly playing with a toy, a miniature horse and wagon fashioned out of wood and straw, but his attention was focused on this man he adored.

"Which wolf story?" Francis asked.

"The one where you were chased."

"Well, Thomas, more than one wolf in these colonies—excuse

me, these states—has lusted after my flesh," he chuckled.

"This would be a northern wolf, sir."

"The northern wolf story you're looking for, is it?" He smiled at Thomas and motioned for the boy to come and sit on his lap, which Thomas scurried to do, leaving his horse and wagon on the floor for more wonderful matters.

"Better still, Bishop," said Sam, "perhaps you could tell us your entire story."

Murmurs of agreement came from Abigail and Nicholas.

"Entire?" Francis tousled Thomas's curly locks. "Well, it's not 'entire' yet," he laughed, "but, yes, I can share some of my story with you."

Francis settled back in his chair, made sure Thomas was comfortable and put a hand to his chin, reflecting on where to begin his tale. He could, of course, begin with his mother's revelation when he was a child. She had a vision that he would be a great preacher and she read Scripture to him one hour a day to prepare him for the task.

Or, he could start when he got saved as a waif of fifteen listening to the stirring preaching of Alexander Mather in Wednesbury in the Black Country of England. Oh, did Francis love the way Mather preached—so personally and confidently; the way he prayed—with feeling and without the use of a book; the way he and the other Methodists sang—with melody and fervor!

Or Francis could begin his story when he started giving Bible readings at his mother's women's meetings. Hm-m-m.

Or, perhaps he should begin with his first ten years of preaching, from the time he was sixteen, circuit-*walking* in England, giving up his job as a metalworker at the age of twenty-one to preach full-time.

No, they wanted to hear about his call to America. And that was a tale that began at the annual Methodist Conference in 1771.

"England!" he exclaimed, startling everyone in the room, even himself. And the memory returned to him as vividly as if it were unfolding before his eyes. He was no longer in this low-ceilinged, pioneer cabin, cozied about with friends before a fireplace. Rather, he was in a cavernous hall whose ceiling rose thirty, forty feet above him. Nearly elbow to elbow, with men and women, dressed in their finery, enthralled at the preaching of John Wesley.

CHAPTER 2

Through Ocean Storms and Sad Departures

Standing at a podium on a platform above the assembly, Wesley, intense and captivating as ever, was describing the New World. A rugged wilderness, most of it. Untested, untried, often unforgiving. Frightening, perhaps most of all, because it was largely unknown, but also because some of the native Indians were dangerous, even murderous. Brave people from Great Britain and continental Europe, looking for a new life with new hopes and dreams, were pouring into the British colonies.

"The fields are ripe for the harvest!" Wesley called out. "Men and women in the cities of Philadelphia and New York; families out in the wilderness, with no preacher to feed them God's Word—our brethren in America call aloud for help! Who will go?"

A chill rippled down Francis' spine and, as his spirit leapt within him, he jumped to his feet. Like a drumbeat in his heart, he knew he should go. If he didn't, the thought of it would bear down upon his soul until he did go, or until he died.

He was twenty-six years old. His life had been lived wholly in and around his parents' cottage in Hamstead Valley—Derbyshire, Staffordshire, Warwickshire, Worcestershire—their green flowing hillsides all he had ever experienced. This was all he knew, these people the only souls he knew. Here was his family, his beloved mother and father. These were people to whom he had preached since he was sixteen. Beyond this? Well, he'd see. No fear, no doubts would hold him back.

He didn't have to steel his courage; it was already steeled within him with a molten passion, a sudden drive to go forward into another chapter of his life!

Shortly afterward, on the night of September third, standing atop a hill outside Port of Pill, where he could see his ship tethered to the wharf and listing easily back and forth atop gentle waves, he preached his last sermon in England. He and one other preacher, Richard Wright, would embark for America the next day.

Looking down on his mother, tears pouring down her cheeks, and dear Emily at her side, weeping so that she would not look up at him, he quoted Psalm 61: "From the end of the earth I will cry unto thee, when my heart is overwhelmed."

He looked down again, to his mother's left where stood his "four affectionate sisters"—sisters in the faith, that is: Phyllis, Bertha, Grace and Rose. Dismayed at his decision, they had pleaded with him to stay in England. He remembered just two days before, reasoning with them all in Phyllis' parents' sitting room. "Why do you think I'm going?" he asked. "To gain honor? To make a fortune? No, if I know my own heart. This is not a frivolous excursion, ladies. I'm going to the New World to live to God and to bring others to do so. Please don't hold me back from such a cause!"

"But who will teach us?" asked Rose, brusquely pushing blonde locks from her face.

"You have no want of other preachers here," Francis said. "In America there has been a work of God; some moving first among the Friends, but in time it declined; likewise by the Presbyterians, but among them also it declined. The people God owns here in England are the Methodists. The doctrines they preach, and the discipline they enforce, are, I believe, the purest of any people in the world. The Lord has greatly blessed these doctrines and this discipline in the three kingdoms. They must therefore be pleasing to Him."

"Yes, but how long must you stay there?" Phyllis asked.

"If God doesn't acknowledge me in America, I'll soon return. And I'll hold you all in my arms, I promise. But," Francis opened his hands as if holding a ball, "if so, I'll be crying in remorse."

Weeping had followed the exchange, and Francis felt now that though these sisters in Christ loved him, their labors that night were only God's work in that they made him strengthen his own resolve.

And now, standing before his last "congregation" before departing, Francis turned his eyes toward Emily, a sweet young flower of a woman for whom he had felt affections that made his heart tremble. If only he were not called to this life, he would offer her his hand in marriage. But—the most heart-rending "but." Because he truly did love her, he could not ask her to follow him to America. What life would that be for her? Sitting at home while he traveled that dangerous new country. Praying for his safety while not knowing. Going to bed alone at night, wondering if he would return. Alone, perhaps feeling forsaken, possibly for days and weeks on end, he didn't know. How could he expose her to that life? In his prayers, he had wept over the decision to simply say his good-byes and wish her well. A simple, "Be well," to a girl he adored?

Yes, he had decided to return in four years, but how could a vivacious young lady wait that long? Could she? Would she? These were questions with which he would not saddle her.

And if he were to ask for her hand, and she did go with him, would he end up as his mentor John Wesley had? With a nipping and nagging wife bellowing at his heels? Making miserable those moments when they were together?

"Where should the missionary herald?" Francis asked his crowd. "To the end of the earth. And whose heart should be overwhelmed, swallowed up, if not the heart of him to whom God has dispensed the Gospel? And where should he seek for living nourishment but to Christ, the Rock that is higher than he? And how should he obtain that nourishment but by constant, fervent prayer?"

The weathered face of his father came into his vision,

moving through the crowd of thirty or forty people toward his mother. Francis glanced down and noticed his father's burly arm, strengthened by years of hard labor as a gardener for the wealthy, reach around his mother's shoulders and pull her to himself. His mother had lost a daughter to sickness when Francis was a child and now she was losing a son to the gospel. She was weeping now, but quietly, and Francis knew well the tender love with which his father embraced her. He knew then that he would be leaving his parents in capable hands—each other's. But he also prayed God's protection on them and Emily and the others as well, for the spiritual climate in England was dark, dark, dark.

A cool breeze swept across Francis' face.

"It's our God's world," he declared, "our God's 'end of the earth,' our God's Word we proclaim, and He—only He—will move in the hearts of men. But who will hear without a preacher? We who are called must go forth, like the disciples and Paul. We must go where men have not heard of God's salvation. Even to face the unknown, we must go. We—must—go!"

Francis looked down at his father and, for the first time in his life, he saw his father weep.

●●●●●

Early the next morning, their departure timed to catch the tide, a contingent of travelers walked the gangplank to board the schooner *North Star*. Salt air filled their nostrils, and luggage hung from their hands, sacks of food—dried fish and tomatoes and the like—over their shoulders, as they hustled along.

Dressed in a new suit his father had given him the day before, Francis studied his companions. An odd mixture of excitement and fear were written on faces of young and old alike.

He captured bits and pieces of hurried conversations as they pushed past him.

"But, Father, I don't want to leave Lynnie and Aunt Molly and Uncle Geoffrey! I don't want to leave all my friends!" The girl was ten or eleven years old. Tears fell in big drops from her eyes and she took no action to wipe them, perhaps to display her displeasure as strongly as she could and change her father's heart.

Her father stopped and squared up to the girl, then bent to his knees to address her eye to eye.

"But this is a new opportunity, Sarah dear," he said soothingly. "Your mother and I have discussed this for months—years. It's a chance to start our lives with clean slates, much like you do in school when you rub the chalkboard clean. We can begin our lives again, rewrite them from a blank canvas."

"But can't you wipe it clean here, Father?" She pleaded, then hugged her father, who picked her up in his arms and hurried off.

"Disappointments! That's all life's given me in this here country!" said a man in harsh dress, tightening fists that had seen many a hard day of labor. In the mines, Francis guessed.

"Ya' can't live with bitterness in your heart," a lady, probably his wife, replied. "That's all ya've ever been—bitter—since I've known ya."

The man pushed his wife along with a grunt. "I weren't raised with a silver spoon in me mouth like these prissy dukes and earls and princes. How did they deserve luxury?"

"T'aint yer bisness. Tis God's."

"You and yer God," he spat and pushed her on again.

A younger couple walked by arm in arm.

"Oh, darling, isn't this exciting?" the woman said.

"Just think!" he replied. "A new adventure!"

A boy, perhaps six years old, wrestled his hand away from his mother's. "But Jesse said it's true, Momma! Sea monsters can swallow us up."

"Don't be silly, child."

"Or a storm at sea might sink us!"

That stumped his mother. How many before them had perished? And, if they did make it, what darkness lurked in the unbroken forests of that new land?

She hesitated, then said, "Child, your papa and I will keep you safe. Trust us!"

The boy whimpered and sought the hand of his father.

One old man turned at the top of the gangplank and gathered a long look at the England he was leaving behind. A tear worked its way down his cheek and sadness deepened the wrinkles around his eyes. He spoke not a word and Francis wondered what his story was.

A little flaxen-haired girl, perhaps five or six years old, held a fistful of wildflowers in one hand and her mother's bejeweled fingers in the other as her father, a well-dressed businessman by the look, hurried them both along. That family could be in trouble, Francis thought, recalling tales he had heard of the rough nature of their destination. It was said America had no "lap of luxury."

"The harvest begins today, with our shipmates, eh?" The voice was that of Richard Wright, and Francis turned to look directly at the young man's smile. He couldn't help but grin himself, even as he glanced back over his shoulder and spotted Emily, a handkerchief to her eyes, along with his mother and father.

Yes! Here was a field white for the harvest, and it was a captive audience—captured for the entire six-week journey to America. And, he prayed, captured by God by the time they docked in Philadelphia.

Francis looked at the new watch his mother had presented to him just an hour before. *Seven-thirty in the morning; time for the new chapter to begin*, he thought.

As the *North Star* set free from the wharf and an east wind filled the ship's sails, Francis could not hear his father, overwhelmed with grief, weep again and cry out, "I shall never see him again!"

Francis could see only the crowd of family and friends, ever diminishing in size, wave to the passengers. Slowly, the entire coast disappeared from sight, replaced eventually by just the blue-green ripples of the vast ocean in the ship's wake.

•••••

The great ship yawning, sounding like rope being pulled through a tight hole, helped put Francis to sleep that night. Despite only a blanket separating him from the wooden floor beneath, he slept well, dreaming of riding a big bay horse over a hilltop. From the sky above, he saw a large hand as big as a house envelop him in protection. He felt exhilaration.

Over the next several days out to sea, Francis, Richard Wright and the other passengers onboard ran to the railing time after time to get sick over the side of the ship. It took awhile for land legs to become sea legs, and choppy seas did not help the matter. Nevertheless, Francis and Wright had made the rounds of the passengers, officers and crew of *North Star*, learning their stories, sharing the gospel and discovering that toughest of all were some of the crew.

Hard life? They lived it. Rough language? They spoke it. Fear of God? Few had it, regardless of the constant knowledge that, any day, disaster could sweep them twenty leagues under the sea. The first mate, Gord, in particular wanted little to do with the two churchmen. A broad, hairy-chested man with a short, salt-and-pepper beard, he scowled at Francis when Francis first offered his hand. "Keep yer God to yerself when you's with me and we'll git along jus fine, mate," he declared between clenched teeth.

"My God is always on my lips, sir, so that will not happen," Francis shot back, then smiled. "But you can plug your ears, if you like."

Gord simply growled and walked off, shouting orders to a deck hand.

Then came Sunday morning, and it arrived with a fury. Gusting winds billowed the huge sails and whipped salt-water spray across the ship's deck. The ocean churned great swelling waves. Captain John Turner—a good man by any reasoning, Francis felt—approached him and said, "Mister Asbury, can't you preach another day?"

"Aye, and every day," Francis replied. "But today, especially. It's the Lord's day, John. I can't put it off."

Turner shook his head, knowing he would make no headway with this young man. He pulled his hat down to his ears to keep it from blowing away and asked, "And you insist on standing—up here on deck?"

Francis nodded.

Turner, at least twenty years his senior, shrugged and offered, "Then I insist that we strap you to the mainmast, so's we don't lose you overboard."

"Strap me in then, John, but I'm preaching today!"

Several minutes later, despite the wind, waves and the sea spray, a goodly crowd sat about the deck bundled up against the cold winds, holding onto whatever they could, including the foremast. Francis, with Richard at his side, led them all in the singing of *Guide Me, O Thou Great Jehovah*.

Then, broadening his stance to steady himself, he opened his Bible to the second chapter of Hebrews and, so as to be heard, loudly read the first three verses: "Therefore we must give the more earnest heed to the things we have heard, lest we drift away. For if the word spoken through angels proved steadfast, and every transgression and disobedience received a just reward, how shall we escape if we neglect so great a salvation, which at the first began to be spoken by the Lord, and was confirmed to us by those who heard Him?"

He looked up just in time to catch a thin film of sea spray across his face. He heard scattered snickering from the ship's crew behind him, but in the faces of the passengers gathered around, there was simply a look of puzzlement—about the scripture he had read.

"If you don't read and meditate on the Word of God," he declared, "you will fall away. Away from His teachings, away from His direction, away from His grace and His protection. If a tinsmith were to disregard his work for years, if a librarian were to walk away from his profession for a period of time, if a ship's mate," he glanced at Gord who stood at quarterdeck, "were to ignore his captain's orders, what would happen to him?"

"He'd be made to walk the gangplank!" hollered a crewman from the rear of the gathering. Laughter erupted.

Francis laughed with them, then looked toward Captain Thomas and called out over the sound of the wind, "Is that true, Captain?"

"Maybe so," Thomas responded, with a crooked smile.

"As with the Lord God," Francis said, "if you ignore His teachings and if you refuse to accept Him as Lord of your life, when you die you will walk the gangplank to hell!

"But that need not be the case. It need not be, my friends. This great salvation that you are neglecting is a free gift from God, and He will continue to extend it, freely, to you. But once you perish…."

Francis allowed that statement to have its effect on the hearts around him. A few moments later, he scanned the people and added, "For those of you who know Him, continue in Him. Unpack your Bibles. Think deeply on its parables. Read diligently its Psalms and Proverbs. Let it increase your faith. Who knows whether you will need to draw on that wisdom at a moment's notice? Who knows when a storm will overtake your life? Do not neglect so great a gift!"

The response seemed lifeless to Francis. He saw no fruit.

Later, Francis and Richard sat on their blankets below deck. "A tough crowd, eh?" Richard said.

Francis smiled dolefully and shrugged. "I'll preach as long as they'll listen, Richard. God is my judge. I simply need to do my duty and leave the harvest to Him."

He kept busy, praying, reading the Bible and other books including Wesley's *Sermons* and Sellon's *The Answer to Elisha Cole on the Sovereignty of God* dispelling the Calvinist argument. A week later, he had an opportunity to again preach on Sunday morning.

It was a calmer sea this day. He didn't have to be strapped in, but instead fixed his back against the mizzen mast. He had discovered through his conversations with them that his listeners were ignorant of God and some were very wicked indeed. Why even come to listen to him? Entertainment? Was that his purpose here? No! It was to speak God's Word and believe that, as the Lord promised, it would "not return void."

He had merely to sow the seed in the morning and in the evening not withhold his hand; and, most importantly, trust the

Lord to draw hearts to Himself.

Quoting from Second Corinthians, Francis declared, "Now, then, we are ambassadors for Christ, as though God did beseech you by us: we pray you in Christ's stead, be reconciled to God."

Hoping instead to reach those before him, Francis indeed felt the power of truth on his own soul. An ambassador for Christ! Be reconciled to God! As an ambassador for the Lord of heavens, he was walking on foreign lands here on earth. And his job was to represent God, share His knowledge, His views, His vision for mankind, and to try to lead the citizens of this world into a new land, a heavenly country, an eternal resting place. As different countries shared treaties with one another, his job as an ambassador of Christ was to reason with men and women to sign on to a covenant with the Lord. A covenant of grace by which they need not give at all, but simply receive—receive the free gift of salvation. He wanted to show them the utter joy that that salvation brings into the heart of a sinner. But at the same time, if and when they became saved, then they were to live as ambassadors of the Holy One and, as such, whatever they said and did was a reflection on His own holiness.

"Do you utter words unworthy of Him Who created you?" Francis asked.

"Do you gossip about your fellow man?

"Do you lurk in the dark shadows of desire for another's goods, another's houses and lands, another's spouse?"

Francis looked up and saw uneasiness stirring among some of the men. He continued on:

"Do you hold something, anything more dearly than knowing your God?

"Do you steal from others or demand usury?

"Do you worship at the altar of money?

"Do you honor your mother and your father?

"Do you ever entertain the thought of murder of a person who has been an enemy—or even desire it in your heart? For even considering such a thing is sin.

"I plead unto you this day, bow your knees to God, bow your

heart to Him, come to His throne room in repentance for your sins. The blood of Christ will wash you clean and God's Holy Spirit will come upon you and create within you a new person. A person worthy to be His ambassador here on Earth. A person *able* to walk as He walked on this Earth."

Francis asked them all to bow their heads and repeat a prayer of repentance. After he had finished, his own spirit mourned within him, and he hungered and thirsted after entire devotion, feeling himself wanting. He himself felt ashamed of many things, which he spoke and did before God and man.

Within his spirit, he cried, "Lord, pardon my manifold defects and failures in duty!"

•••••

Little Thomas Brackett stirred on Francis' lap and the bishop was disconnected from his recollections. He looked down at the boy, who was fighting to stifle a huge yawn. Francis laughed. "Well, it appears I've served one purpose: putting Thomas to sleep, eh?"

"No, sir. No, sir," the boy responded. "Go on. Go on."

Sam Brackett rose from his chair. "No, Son, it's time you be off to bed. Perhaps the bishop will continue his story tomorrow. He'll be with us three days, you know."

Sam looked questioningly toward Francis, and Francis smiled and nodded assent. "Of course."

A half-hour later, as the others lay in their beds, Francis sat in a padded chair before the fireplace. Ah, now, this was comfort beyond the norm! He thought of the myriad nights spent in flea-infested sheds and barns, sleeping on boards and nothing else except perhaps a little straw to ease the hardness. Fleas, mosquitoes, bugs of sorts he had not known in England—they all assailed him, taunting him to return to the cities of Philadelphia, or Boston where there were at least panes of glass to help keep out the flying, blood-sucking critters.

Watching the red and yellow flames flicker before him, he

chuckled, remembering the nights—two, or was it three? Well, several at least—when he had fallen off his horse from sheer exhaustion. *I might fall off this chair tonight*, he thought, *but at least it would be onto a soft landing on this bear rug beside me.... Not on a patch of brambles, or tree roots sticking out of the forest ground.*

He thought again of the apostle Paul. *Ah, Paul, how I will enjoy sharing experiences with you in heaven! A man after my own heart. A man who never slowed down—until you were imprisoned, that is.*

He commiserated with Paul, who wrote in II Corinthians 11:25-27:

"... Three times I was shipwrecked, a night and a day I have been in the deep, in journeys often, in perils of waters, in perils of robbers, in perils of my own countrymen, in perils of the Gentiles, in perils in the city, in perils in the wilderness, in perils in the sea, in perils among false brethren; in weariness and toil, in sleeplessness often, in hunger and thirst, in fastings often, in cold and nakedness—besides the other things, what comes upon me daily: my deep concern for all the churches."

Besides the shipwreck—and he came close to that, too—Francis had experienced all this and he felt a warm companionship with Paul, a sort of alliance of the miserable.

He could swap stories with Paul, that he had been chased by savage wolves; hidden in a swamp for three days while soldiers searched for him; shot at by highwaymen (he gingerly tapped his skull, making sure that this day's bullet had indeed missed its mark); bruised by saplings, bitten by mosquitoes and drenched with malaria vapors. He escaped the ravages of yellow fever, and had been pelted by hailstones of such size that three of them filled a pint measure.

He fell asleep, sitting on the chair, with pleasant thoughts that, even if hail did pummel the woods tonight, he could relax comfortably before the still-crackling embers of a warm fire.

CHAPTER 3

The Plague of "Cityitis"

When Abigail Brackett swished down the stairs to prepare breakfast for her family and guests at the crack of dawn, she found Francis sitting in a window chair reading his Bible. She wasn't surprised, knowing that he awoke every morning at four o'clock to read the Scriptures and pray, that he often preached at five o'clock, and spent at least four hours a day in the Holy Book. She recalled his words the first time he ever spent a night with them: "Dear sister, if a man is truly called of God to preach His Word, that man must immerse himself in it. Sometimes I swim in it. Sometimes I breeze through it with a racer's stroke. Sometimes I float about, soaking it in. But, as Mister Wesley says, we must devote hours a day to study; and I live by that demand."

"Ah, Francis!" Abigail said. "Again you rise before me. I'll put some coffee on the stove immediately."

Francis smiled up at his host. "You're an angel, Abigail."

Sam, two-stepping down the stairs, overheard Francis and declared, "Indeed she is, Francis. Sent from heaven."

Abigail laughed lightly.

A few minutes later, as the aroma of coffee wafted through the home, a sleepy Nicholas Snethen stumbled from a first-floor bedroom beyond the kitchen. A look of shame covered his face and he tried to avoid Francis' eyes, knowing Wesley's four-hour-a-day rule. Sleeping as late as six o'clock did not bode well for fulfilling that rule.

"Sorry, bishop," Nicholas said. "I've overslept."

"Diligence, Nicholas, that's all I ask." Francis looked at his aide with the love of a father. He knew it couldn't be easy for a young man to travel with an old fellow so set in his ways, so demanding of himself. Of course, he didn't expect Nicholas to keep up Francis' own schedule; but he did expect him to mature and set one of his own.

Abigail started the cooking-stove fire. Francis had blown almost-dead ambers to life in the fireplace and rekindled that fire when he awoke. Now Sam stoked the flames hotter still. A half-hour later, they were all enjoying breakfast—even little Thomas, who had dragged a chair up next to Francis and asked what he was going to preach on this morning.

"Well, young Thomas, I've softened in my later years," Francis said. "I'll speak what the Spirit of God leads me to, and I believe it will deal with sanctification, that is, how God enables us to separate ourselves from the things of the world that distract us from His will and a close relationship with Him. God's your friend, you know, not some fiend up there in the sky waiting for you to sin so that He might whip you about for awhile. He sits on His heavenly throne cheering you on, nudging you toward right decisions, ready to comfort you when you scrape your knee, or when bullies set upon you."

"What do you mean you've 'softened'?" Thomas asked, poking at a piece of sausage.

"Well, Thomas, I want people to get better acquainted with their loving Father and to know Him as that—just as you do your own dad. But I didn't always preach this way."

Francis remembered the day their ship landed at port in Philadelphia. It was on October 27, cold and blustery. He and Richard Wright were surprised at the city.

Cobblestone streets were chock full of people, dressed as though they were in London, bustling about their business.

"Certainly no outpost, this," Richard said as they carried their luggage from the wharf into the crowd.

Francis noticed the street lamps lining what he could see of the nearby streets. "It appears that Philadelphia has all the comforts of England."

"And a bit of the smell, too," Richard said, his nose wrinkling at the result of open sewage.

Francis nodded, then stopped a man in the street. "Smith Street?"

The man pointed vaguely in a direction and strode on.

"Pleasant chap," Richard drolled.

"At least he knows his directions," Francis smiled, squinting to see a signpost down the street a ways. "I think that's Smith Street, there, on the right."

"Then that is where our hosts live," Richard said.

"Frank and Elizabeth Harris," Francis recited from a slip of paper in his hand. "A fine Christian couple, I hear."

"Well, we'll only inconvenience them for one night."

"Ah, to sleep on something other than wood!"

"I'm finding it a bit difficult to walk on firm ground," Richard laughed. "I'll probably fall off a stationary bed."

A few minutes later, knocking on the red door at the brick house, Francis and Richard were greeted by a short, thin lady in her early fifties, with a wide smile bracketed by curl upon curl of red hair falling to her shoulders. "Pastors Wright and Asbury!"

"Yes!" Francis and Richard caught her joy.

"Please, I'm Francis and this is Richard," Francis said.

"Enter. Enter!" She turned aside and swung the door open. They followed her lead and stepped inside. "I'm Elizabeth Harris." She offered her hand, then looked back toward a flight of stairs behind her. "Rejoice!"

"Pardon?" Francis looked at Elizabeth in puzzlement. She returned his look, then realized his question. "Oh, *Rejoice* is our daughter's name."

Again, calling up the staircase. "Rejoice! Come meet our guests!"

A girl so pretty she would rival Emily swept to the top of the stairs. Dressed in a gown that would stand her well in high English society, she nearly flew down the stairway. At the bottom of the stairs, she curtseyed deeply.

"My dear," Elizabeth scolded, "Mister Asbury and Mister Wright are missionaries, not the King."

"I would say a visit from missionaries surpasses that of the King, Mama," she replied, her eyebrows rising in fun. Rejoice's red hair fell like rivulets along a face that was like porcelain, with a thin nose and sparkling green eyes. Francis gauged that she was aptly named.

Her lips curling into a smile, Elizabeth simply shook her head in resignation. Introducing her daughter to their guests, she looked at a large grandfather clock in the parlor and declared, "My husband, Frank, will be home in one hour. Rejoice, show our guests to their room and prepare them basins with water with which to refresh themselves."

Rejoice, as if carried by angels' feet, led them up the staircase in the large house.

•••••

An hour later, the man of the house having arrived, the family and guests sat around a mahogany dining table. Francis heard the noises of a kitchen in full swing through a rear door to the room and could smell chicken baking, the aroma so appetizing he could almost taste it. His stomach, deprived of good food for weeks, growled in expectation. A short, stout woman entered the room, a large plate in her hand containing a good-sized chicken.

"Thank you, Candace," Frank Harris said. "Before you deliver the meal, I want you to meet our guests."

Hearing who they were, Candace declared, "Dear sirs, welcome to America!"

"Why, thank you, dear lady!" Francis replied.

"We're excited to be here," Richard added.

"May the good Lord bless your stay," Candace smiled.

When she returned to the kitchen to gather the rest of the meal, Elizabeth explained, "Candace is with us for only a short time longer. We paid for her passage here to the colonies under the agreement that she'd repay us with five-years service as our cook."

"And a fine cook she has been!" Frank Harris said.

"And a good friend, too," Rejoice said. "She'll join us tonight at the church."

Moments later, the blessing said and the group enjoying a delicious meal, Francis ventured, "Mister Harris, all that we have heard about the spiritual needs of the colonies has been the opinion of people in England. What do you think?"

"It's Frank, please, Francis." Accepting a nod of approval from Francis, Frank Harris set down a forkful of chicken and twisted a rather long moustache. Looking straight at Francis, he said, "In seventeen hundred and thirty-nine George Whitefield arrived here in Philadelphia. His powerful preaching led many to God. I know. I was a teenager then and I was one of his converts. With the help of Whitefield's good friend, Benjamin Franklin, and others enough money was raised to build a large hall to host speakers on religion."

"That's exciting," Richard said. Francis noticed that Richard's eyes were not even on Frank Harris but on Rejoice. He was smitten.

"Yes, it was," Harris said. "The problem was—and is to this day—that preachers would not leave Philadelphia. And we hear the same from people we know in New York City and Boston."

"But, dear," Elizabeth said, "almost everybody lives in, or next to, the cities."

"But what of those who don't, Liz?" Harris replied. "Probably two out of every ten of us live away from the coastline. Are we to give them over to Satan?"

"Of course not."

"Well, Francis asked about the state of religion here, and I see the greatest need outside the cities."

"Modern comforts," Francis said and looked about the table. "Modern comforts can be a problem. Not only will comfortable living entice preachers to remain where they have them, it can lead to comfortable preaching.

"As much as I'm looking forward to cuddling up to some of that comfort tonight, in a real bed, I know the Lord does not want me to get used to it."

Richard cringed. "I know my brother well. Good thing he's got a high tolerance for pain."

Laughter greeted his remark.

•••••

An hour later, the Harris family, Francis and Richard joined scores of worshipers walking up the wide steps of St. George's Church, a large structure that the Dutch Reformed Church erected in 1763 and which the Methodist Society purchased and dedicated in 1769. Its broad oak doors were open and, through the crowd before him, Francis caught glimpses of Joseph Pilmoor at the entrance, welcoming everyone individually.

Finally they reached the door.

"Brother Asbury!" Pilmoor declared, "I've been here six years, so it's been six-and-a-half since I've seen you." Shorter than Francis by two or three inches, he raised his hands upon Francis' shoulders and looked him over. "Welcome to America, Frankie!" With that, he latched onto Francis with a big hug. Looking over Francis' shoulder, he noticed Richard.

"And this must be Brother Wright?"

"Sir." Richard extended his hand.

"Joseph," Pilmoor corrected. "We're brothers in arms, Brother Wright. Equals. Side by side."

"It's Richard, then." Richard smiled at Pilmoor, a broad, well-dressed man in his early thirties. "I'm excited to hear you preach tonight."

"Well, you won't be hearing me preach tonight. But I promise you'll not be disappointed. Tonight, Captain Thomas Webb is giving a word."

Francis' ears perked up. "Webb?" he asked.

"A veteran of the French and Indian War," Pilmoor responded.

"He was instrumental in our purchase of the church building. He's a man you'll not soon forget."

Indeed, Pilmoor was not mistaken.

Sitting in a seat in the Harris family pew, Francis had to look about him to make sure he wasn't in a theater. Before him, in the pulpit, stood a man who would rival Shakespeare's Falstaff as a memorable character. Webb could easily have been born in Stratford-upon-Avon, in the brilliant mind of Sir William. While Falstaff was, in one play a comic, in another an opportunist, and in another a non-judgmental father substitute, Captain Thomas Webb was none of these. But, Francis thought, he might—like Falstaff—be larger than life.

Already a tall man, when Webb stepped up the stairs to the pulpit after Pilmoor's invocation, he towered even higher still than the churchgoers seated below him. He was dressed in a red uniform that Francis could not quite place; a military garb, perhaps? And he wore a black patch over one eye; the eye lost in the war, probably? As Francis pondered these questions, his breath nearly escaped him. With one swift, experienced motion, Captain Webb swept the sword from its sheath that hung at his hip. Several women and young people gasped. Webb then pointed it skyward, as if giving tribute to a Heavenly Being, and then, ever so calmly, laid it gently across the front of the pulpit. Candlelight glinted faintly off its sharp edge.

"Ha! To be in God's house!" Webb exclaimed.

"Amen!" came the reply from many seated about the hall.

With his one eye, Webb looked expansively over the congregation.

"If you have enthusiasm for your work, fervor for your family, you must have zeal for God Almighty!" Webb declared.

"Amen!" came the response.

Opening the oversized Bible on the pulpit, he flipped through its pages. "Join me at Ecclesiastes chapter nine, verse ten," he said, then read: "'Whatever your hand finds to do, do it with all your might, for in the grave, where you are going, there is neither working nor planning nor knowledge nor wisdom.'

"Now to the New Testament, Romans chapter twelve, verse eleven." Waiting just a moment for people to find the passage, this red-coated bear of a man read on: "'Be not lagging in diligence, fervent in spirit, serving the Lord.'"

Raising his eye from the Bible to the congregation, Webb asked, "Do we understand 'zeal'? Do we understand the zeal our Lord Jesus had when He upset the tables of the money lenders and drove them from the synagogue because they defiled God's house? How His disciples recalled the psalmist's words: 'Zeal for my Father's house has consumed me'?

"I want to stress two things tonight: act and do it with zeal!

"No man has ever won a war lackadaisically. Even when God went before the Hebrews, they were not apathetic, lazy, half-hearted in the security that God would fight their battle—even though they believed He would. When Joshua and the Hebrews circled Jericho that seventh day, they didn't simply say, 'Let's take a seat right here, Delilah, and watch the Lord beat up on Jericho.'

"No! They shouted aloud! They were zealous! People could probably hear them back in Jerusalem!"

Webb chuckled, and then, with a flourish, lifted his sword, circled it before him and pierced an unseen foe. "Yes, I fought some battles, and I fought them with zeal, piercing a few enemy in the fray. But, one enemy, fighting with zeal, pierced me right back!" He pointed to his eye patch. "That is why, in Ephesians chapter six when Paul writes about wearing the armor, most all of it's defensive armor.

"Let's read it together." All the church rifled through their Bibles to the Epistle to the Ephesians, and Webb read, beginning at verse ten: "'Finally, be strong in the Lord and in His mighty power. Put on the full armor of God so that you can take your stand against the devil's schemes. For our struggle is not against flesh and blood, but against the rulers, against the authorities, against the powers of this dark world and against the spiritual forces of evil in the heavenly realms.

"'Therefore put on the full armor of God, so that when the day of evil comes, you may be able to stand your ground, and after you have done everything, to stand. Stand firm then, with the belt of truth buckled around your waist, with the breastplate of righteousness in place, and with your feet fitted with the readiness that comes from the gospel of peace. In addition to all this, take up the shield of faith, with which you can extinguish all the flaming arrows and the evil one.…'" Webb paused for emphasis, then continued, "'Take the helmet of salvation and sword of the Spirit, which is the Word of God,'" and he flashed his sword again.

"Ladies and gentlemen, God Almighty wants us to go forth with our armor on, wielding the sword of the Spirit, and doing all that we do for Him with enthusiasm. Fervor. Passion. Zeal!"

Pointing to Francis and Richard, Webb reiterated to the congregation, "With zeal! The type of zeal that these two young men have displayed by leaving family, friend and church. By sailing halfway around the world to unfamiliar people, an odd country and a dangerous wilderness.

"For what purpose? To spread the gospel! Armed with what? The sword of God: His Word! With what attitude? Zealousness!"

A shiver flashed down Francis' spine.

"How many of us walk in the boldness and zeal that God desires? Let all of us who do, raise our hands."

No one, not even Webb, raised a hand. Webb appeared to get an inspiration and, stepping down from the pulpit, called Pilmoor to him. They consulted in whispers for several seconds, then Pilmoor nodded assent. Webb raised his one, piercing eye to Francis and Richard and said, "Young men, will you join us up here in front of the congregation?"

Francis and Richard slid out of the Harris pew and stepped forward to stand in front of Pilmoor and Webb.

Pilmoor looked across the congregation. "Will you all stand and join us in a prayer for these two men who have come from England to spread God's Word?"

Francis heard scuffling behind him and saw people standing in his peripheral vision. Pilmoor stepped around behind the two of them and placed one hand solidly on Francis' shoulder to his left and Richard's to his right. Webb, standing before them, placed one hand on each man's forehead.

"As the apostle Paul told Timothy," said Webb, "we encourage you, Brother Asbury and Brother Wright, 'fan into flame the gift of God!' Fan that flame of the evangelist that burns within you, brothers. And do what Isaiah, in chapter fifty-nine, tells us that God did. 'He put on righteousness as His breastplate, and the helmet of salvation on His head; He put on the garments of vengeance and wrapped Himself in zeal as in a cloak.'"

Locking his eye first on Francis and then Richard, Webb resumed, "As soldiers in God's army, go forth with zeal, not in your flesh but in the power of His Spirit. Our enemy, Satan, will attack you with violence from other men, with assaults from nature, even with criticism from the Body of Christ. But stand firm in the faith, brothers. These colonies are depending on you and men like you to fill men's hearts with the love and compassion of our Lord and Savior.

"God has a mighty right arm. March forward in that protection, with the Almighty as your High Tower and with Christ as the Cornerstone of your faith."

With that, Pilmoor invited the congregation forward to welcome Francis and Richard and encourage them on their mission to the colonies.

Francis was overwhelmed. All these people! Welcoming them! It appeared they hardly knew how to show their love sufficiently, bidding Francis and Richard welcome with fervent affection and receiving them as angels of God. *Oh, that we may always walk worthy of the vocation to which we are called*, Francis thought.

•••••

The next morning, Frank Harris had an early-morning business appointment and handed them each an envelope on his way out the door, wishing them well and saying his home was always open to them. Francis and Richard thanked him heartily, resisting the urge to open their envelopes. At church the previous night they had been astonished when, after they were prayed over, Joseph

Pilmoor had taken an offering for them. The congregation had been very generous. Frank Harris' gift this morning was blessing heaped upon blessing. Neither of the men knew how much financial support they would receive in the years ahead of them, but they guessed it would be meager.

About mid-morning, as a mist began to fall, Elizabeth and Rejoice accompanied Francis and Richard to the nearby livery, where they boarded a stagecoach to New York City. Having two wonderful Christian women see them off was yet another blessing and Francis could only guess how much impact Rejoice had had on Richard's heart in such a brief time. He did, however, get an inkling from the expression on Richard's face when he bowed to kiss Rejoice's hand in farewell. Rejoice's smile was infectious.

On the roadway, called The King's Path, Richard was silent, reflective.

"A pretty girl, eh?" Francis said.

"Pretty, and sweet enough to win my heart in about two seconds." Richard sounded more morose than joyful.

"Keep the relationship before the Lord, Richard, and I will, too."

Richard, seated across from Francis, smiled forlornly at him. "I'm called here for God's work, Francis, not for affairs of the heart."

"Do you think God doesn't know that?"

"You're a good brother, Francis." Richard patted his arm and pretended to doze off into a nap. The King's Path was wide and relatively flat, but the bumps would deprive even the dead of sleep, Francis guessed. As they traveled, they passed men on horseback or aboard Conestoga wagons. Francis had never seen these before. Men and women were aboard open wagons as well, and more than a few of the light, fashionable coaches so popular with the wealthy of England. In Great Britain, upholsterers, carvers, gilders—even painters, lacquer workers and glazers—cooperated to produce family coaches and others for weddings and funerals as well as light and comfortable conveyances. *They must have counterparts here in the colonies*, Francis thought.

What would he ride? A simple horse would be preferable. No wheels necessary! *The only thing that could break down would be the horse—and me,* he thought.

A day later, the coach arrived in New York. "Stage coach, mail coach, whatever you call these contraptions, never ever again am I riding one," Francis declared as they jumped down to solid ground.

Gathering their luggage, they set off to find Richard Boardman, who was General Assembly representative to Wesley and in sole command of the Methodist work in the New World.

New York City was bustling, filled with wagons, coaches, carts, buggies—and people—lots of people. *This is no outpost, either*, Francis thought.

On a side road, John Street, near the outskirts of the community, they found Boardman—a large, boisterous, congenial young man, about Francis' age, who welcomed them with open arms and led them to a spare room in his house for them to share with Richard Sause, another young Methodist preacher.

"Make yourself comfortable. Get unpacked and settled. I'll introduce you around to the other ministers in town."

"Ministers … 'in town'?" Francis asked.

Boardman smiled broadly. "Oh, yes, perhaps a dozen of them of different persuasions."

"Where do they preach?"

"Why, here in New York City, of course." Boardman's brow knit.

"What about those in the countryside?"

Boardman looked at him dumbly. "Countryside?"

"I'll be back," Francis said. Grabbing a small satchel, he headed out the door.

"Where's he going?" Boardman asked Richard. Richard could only shrug an "I-don't-know."

In the city! Francis nearly shouted to himself as he walked out the door and tromped down the road. *In the city!?*

This confirmed what Frank Harris had said.

Behind him, standing in his doorway, Boardman put his hands

to his hips and shook his head, wondering what possessed Francis to charge out of the house. Richard, standing beside him, didn't have to wonder; he knew.

Francis was on a mission, a mission to find a livery, hire a horse and leave the comfort of New York City—leave it to, well, those who wanted to be comfortable in life.

Turning a corner, he bumped into a very tall, very thin young man. Francis' first thought was of a beanstalk. But the fellow caught himself from stumbling backwards and called out, "Hi-ho!"

"Oh, I'm sorry," Francis said.

"You're in a hurry. Can I help?"

"I'm looking for a livery."

Pointing the longest finger Francis had ever seen in the direction of a far street corner, the man said, "Turn right at the silversmith sign and you'll run right into it."

"Thank you." Francis turned to go, but the man cut in, "By the way, my name's Sause, Richard Sause."

The name caught Francis' attention. "The Richard Sause who lives with the Reverend Mister Boardman?"

"One and the same."

Francis introduced himself, told Richard of his intentions and, before he knew it, he had a companion.

Minutes later, the two young men were riding beside one another along The Shore Road on the way to Westchester, some twenty miles from New York City. It was late afternoon. Two hours later, each knew enough about the other that they would become lifelong friends.

Suddenly, coming around a huge oak tree, they noticed buildings up ahead in the fading light. As they came closer they spotted a "Town Hall" sign on a large white building. A light shone out of a second-floor window and townspeople were meandering down the street toward the building in twos and fours, teenagers and adults, and entering through the front door.

Francis and Richard tethered their horses to a railing and hung grain bags from the horses' necks.

Francis pulled his Bible from his saddlebag, but Richard held out empty hands. "I'm unarmed."

"That's all right, Richard. I've got enough fire power for an army here," Francis said, pointing to his well-worn leather volume.

They stepped briskly along the sidewalk—their destination, that second-floor light. People must be gathering to hear the Word!

Francis and Sause hurried through the front door and followed others up wide stairs along the right side of the building. They could hear musicians beginning to tune stringed instruments upstairs. *No organ? Worship music with other instruments? What fun!* At the top of the stairs was a wide hallway. At the far end was the top of the other stairway that wound up the left side of the building. To the right were wide doors opening into a hall. Dozens of people gathered in groups, chatting about this and that, apparently waiting to … to . . .

Sause turned to Francis. "A dance!" he declared.

"Not for long!" Francis replied. He stepped quickly through groups of revelers toward the back of the hall and when he arrived where the chamber members sat in their straight-back chairs, he turned and called out, "I know you all are waiting for the music of Franz Joseph Haydn and Theodore Pachelbel. But, beforehand, I have melodies of another kind for your ears." He held high his Bible and declared, "The Lord is speaking to us tonight, right here in this room!"

A sprinkling of jeers from people more anxious to dance was drowned out by "Hear-hear's" around the hall. Francis knew then that he had an audience.

Opening the Bible to the book of Acts, he read from the seventeenth chapter, thirtieth verse: "But God now commands all men everywhere to repent."

He looked at the dancers-turned-congregation. That single sentence may have quickly dissolved that audience. They didn't look especially repentant. He scanned the band to his right. Well, they didn't appear so, either, but everyone at least was listening.

"John the Baptist," he said, "came declaring, 'Repent, for the kingdom of God is near.' Jesus Christ came declaring, 'Repent, for the kingdom of God is near.' Paul and the apostles went throughout the known world preaching, 'Repent, for the kingdom of God is near.'

"I ask you simply, Have you done so? Do you do so? Daily?"

A few heads nodded assent. Francis plowed on, his voice rising: "Do you really? Do you come to the Lord and confess the ugly blackness of your soul? Do you kneel at His cross and ask forgiveness for loose lips, gossiping, profane language, petty bickering, bitterness, unforgiveness for a wrong done? Do you weep between the pew and the altar for all the opportunities you had to do good and did not do it?

"I ask, do you ever look within yourself, at your own soul, and see that the fine upstanding person you feel you are, is not there at all? This evening, when you dressed for this dance, did you look in the mirror and realize that you are indeed a sinner? Did you see the reflection of a man or woman bound for the gates of heaven—or the fires of hell?

"Can you feel the flames licking at your boots?" Francis called out. "Can you see the devil licking his lips in anticipation of your arrival?"

The men before Francis were fidgeting. Many had turned their eyes away and were staring at their boots, or a dead moth on the floor—anywhere but at him. It was deadly silent.

Francis searched for eyes to lock onto and found those of a man twenty years his senior trying his best to hold back a trickle of tears and to wipe them from his cheek without his neighbors noticing. Francis eyed him. "Do you think that somehow you can, at the least, live this life in your sins and thus put off God's judgment?"

Francis scanned the crowd. "Do you know the story of Sodom and Gomorrah?"

Some of the bowed heads looked up—acknowledgement in their eyes.

"They were cities of rampant sin and wickedness. The hearts

of their inhabitants were evil, filled with wild passions, bent on adultery, rape, child molestation, blood lust … murder."

Francis flipped the pages of his Bible to Genesis chapter nineteen and read verses twenty-four and twenty-five: "'Then the Lord rained brimstone and fire on Sodom and Gomorrah, from the Lord out of the heavens. So He overthrew those cities, all the plain, all the inhabitants of the cities, and what grew on the ground.'"

He motioned toward the town outside the four walls of the hall. "Is it possible this is our Sodom or Gomorrah? Do you not think it possible that a holy God has seen and heard enough? That He knows the dark hearts of the souls here? That He, in one flick of a finger, will not cause the earth to open up and swallow us whole, or the sky to blow open and rain down fire from the heavenlies to consume this place—and every one of us with it?

"Yes, it's true what men say: God *is* a God of love. But, to their detriment, they add, 'So he won't destroy us.'

"Yet I declare to you this day: God *is* love. But His love can not embrace what His holiness can not endure! I repeat: His love can not embrace what His holiness can not endure!"

Every eye in the hall was upon Francis. Palms were sweating. Fear pulsed through men's hearts. A slim young lady halfway back in the hall fainted. At the same moment, a large man perhaps six feet from Francis surged forward toward him. "How must I repent? How must I repent!?" he asked, tears pouring down his cheeks. Others pushed forth beside and behind him. Men and women alike wept aloud. Noses were blown into handkerchiefs.

Sause looked on in amazement from several yards to Francis' left. He had never heard such a thing, never seen anyone preach with such authority, never witnessed people spring to their feet as if they were at the judgment bar of God!

Francis turned to Sause and said softly, "Richard, I need your help to minister repentance and salvation to these people."

Hours later, the last of the crowd, her hands raised, tears of joy coursing down her cheeks, walked from the hall, her husband beside her holding her steady. Even the band members had come forward. There was no dancing that night for the townspeople of

Westchester.

Leaving the hall, Francis and Sause found a boarding house with a spare room. The next morning at four o'clock, the sky still dark outside, Francis rose from his bed and dressed. An hour later, Sause awoke to see his new friend reading the Bible by lamp light at a chair in the corner of the room.

"With some breakfast in our bellies we can ride off to that other town you mentioned to me—West Farms," Francis said.

"With breakfast in my belly, I must return to New York City," Sause said. "I've business to attend to back home."

Francis nodded assent.

"But," Sause said, "I thought you would stay here today to preach again tonight. So many people asked that you do so."

"Oh, I shall. But I can preach today in West Farms, then return here by evening. It's not that far, right?"

Sause shook his head in wonder. "No, Francis, it's not that far."

•••••

"Bishop Asbury," Sam Brackett interjected, "I hate to interrupt, but if we're going to make it to church in time, we'd better be getting on."

Francis looked around the kitchen table and he was back in 1809. He looked down at his hands. No longer the strong hands of a young man. He felt the crimp in his knees—from the rheumatism that assailed him—and the ache in his chest from bouts of pleurisy and asthma. The repeated drenchings and cold winds that had assaulted him on his travels up and down the colonies had, at times, grotesquely swollen his feet and had assigned him to bed. He had grumbled that he was a worthless lump of misery and sin, unworthy of the attention people had given him. But he had been feeling better lately, much better—given a second life, perhaps. *Certainly those highwaymen had found no easy target, eh? Ha!*

A half-hour later, a congregation packed cheek by jowl waited in anticipation of hearing the famous Bishop Francis Asbury preach. Many had heard him before. Others hadn't. But they all knew who he was. Why wasn't it his picture on the coins of the new country? He was, after all, more recognizable to Americans than George Washington, Benjamin Franklin, John Adams, James Monroe.... A college had been named after him and Thomas Coke. Had any been named for Franklin, Washington, or Monroe? When Asbury crossed the Allegheny Mountains, he was protected by as many as fifty armed men. Were Jackson or Adams so guarded?

Introduced by the church's pastor, Reverend Robert Matthews, Francis stood before them. When the words "Dear children" passed his lips, those who had heard him when he was a younger man knew that a transformed person spoke this day. And when he opened his Bible and spoke the grace-filled words "God, who is rich in mercy, made us alive with Christ even when we were dead in transgressions," they were touched at his transformation.

How many souls had he won to Christ preaching hell-and-damnation? Tens of thousands, perhaps hundreds of thousands. How many souls would he win preaching love-and-grace? As he preached on, they figured probably just as many. Why? Because one reality was striking in both presentations: the time was always now, this moment, to accept the Lord, for not one person in the world knew what would happen to him even this very day, this very hour. Hell and damnation were terrible realities. And, it was also true that God's love and grace were extended to all men this very moment. But people still had to accept that free gift.

Listening from the Brackett family pew three rows from the front of the church, Sam thought on these things. And he recalled something he had recently read, written by one of Asbury's colleagues: "Bishop Asbury can be a son of thunder *and* of consolation."

Today, he was a son of consolation. Sam leaned his ear toward Francis as—in a deep-toned, mellow-bass voice that sounded like a dulcimer—he quoted Romans 8:38: "For I am persuaded that neither death nor life, nor angels nor principalities nor powers, nor things present nor things to come, nor height nor depth, nor any other created thing, shall be able to separate us from the love of

God which is in Christ Jesus our Lord."

That afternoon, Francis, Nicholas and the Bracketts all dined at the Reverend Robert and Deborah Matthews' cottage. Afterwards, sitting in the large parlor and waiting for the six o'clock service, little Thomas asked Francis to continue his story. Francis looked at the pastor who nodded approval, then resumed his narrative.

"I found a new disease here in America," he said from his fireside chair.

"A new disease?" Abigail asked.

"Yes," Francis smiled wryly. "I called it 'cityitis.' I returned from that first trip to Westchester, West Farms, New Rochelle, Rye and East Chester and I was full of fire! These people in the countryside were ready to be harvested!

"I know that some listened just for entertainment. But I wasn't about to perform magic tricks, or do a song and dance. I was firing forth the Word of God, and we know it does not return void, eh?" He smiled down at Thomas, who had taken a spot on the floor next to Francis' feet.

"I gave the Reverend Boardman a full report, gushing over with hope and suggesting we create some circuits for our ministers to ride, as we had in England, but he squashed the idea. Upset that I had left, he insisted we all remain in the city. It was monstrous! But the reasons were obvious. People were addicted to fashionable clothing, and there was an air of gaiety everywhere, which was distressing. Oh, trouble was at hand. Winter was approaching and we preachers were about to be shut up in the cities. I could feel claustrophobia—spiritual claustrophobia—inching up and over me. I didn't fear Reverend Boardman; I feared God and His displeasure.

"Recall what God said to the Hebrews through Joshua in Joshua chapter eighteen: 'How long will you neglect to go and possess the land which the Lord God of your fathers has given you?' Well, He wanted us to 'possess' this land, America, with the gospel of Christ!"

Francis reflected on those early days in America.

Revolutionary talk pervaded the city streets and country lanes.

England was oppressing the colonies, stealing away their goods across the ocean and loading taxation on these people with a heavy boot. They had a difficult enough time surviving in a hostile environment without having to worry whether they could afford every new tax piled upon a stack of old ones.

Walking through Boston in late October of 1773, Francis witnessed the growing fury firsthand. Having arrived in the city just after three pirates had been hanged on Boston Commons, he discovered that the crowds had gathered elsewhere. But the sport of hanging pirates was replaced by something more political— and more disarming.

The ocean tide had ebbed and instead of its waves lurking near Kilby Street and threatening the city's famous Bunch of Grapes Tavern, it left behind mud flats and the smells of hard-shell clams, crabs, urchins, and what-have-you. Somewhere nearby, something—a pig, perhaps?—was rotting in the mud.

In an earlier visit to Boston, Francis had seen a dead cat or two floating in the stagnant waters of Mill Pond and wondered when this city would ever be made modern, with its swamps filled in. It seemed to survive solely by its link to the ocean, and thus as a harbor for goods from Great Britain and Europe.

Making his way into the North End of the city, Francis could hear a crowd before he saw it. Then he turned a corner onto Union Street where stood The Green Dragon Tavern, infamous as a haunt for revolutionaries. Hundreds and hundreds of people— many obviously laborers but some dressed in velvet and ruffles, wearing powdered hair and periwigs—gathered at a street corner, huddled against the wind. They were listening to a man, flanked by a woman on each side, harangue against England.

"Because the East India Company is on the verge of bankruptcy, does the British government have the right to give it tax privileges above us in the colonies?" he asked.

The crowd, a goodly number of women included, hollered, "No!"

"Do our merchants deserve to be treated thus?"

Again, "No!"

"Is it right that the East India Company can give some importers lucrative rights—even leading to a monopoly—that others don't possess?"

"No!"

Francis nudged a man next to him and asked, "Who's this?"

"Why, John Adams, sir," the man replied incredulously as if the person asking must be a nitwit.

Francis turned back and concentrated on this man who held his audience in such rapt attention. His graying hair indicated he was perhaps in his early 50s. Palsied hands twitched constantly, almost violently sometimes. But his voice betrayed no weakness, no lack of confidence, no shortcoming in oratory.

Adams continued: "His Magesty and his Parliament have determined to tax the colonies to recoup their war costs, or just to prove their dominance." The comment was met with a hiss from the crowd.

"It began with the Molasses Act back in seventeen hundred and thirty-three." Another hiss.

"It persisted with the Sugar Act in seventeen-sixty-four, designed to pay for England's debt from the French and Indian War." Again, a hiss.

"The Stamp Act in seventeen-sixty-five." Yet another hiss.

"Then the Townsend Acts in seventeen-sixty-seven." Hiss.

"Then the duty on tea!" Hiss.

"And shall we ever, ever forget the Boston Massacre just three years ago?"

An explosive, "No!" was the answer.

"The arrogance of the Crown and Parliament in believing they can dictate our policies, an ocean and a thousand leagues distant, is repulsive and revolting," Adams declared. "Can it be said with any color of truth and justice, that this continent of three thousand miles in length, and of a breadth as yet unexplored, possessing some five million people, has the least voice, vote, or influence in the British Parliament?"

Grumbles of discontent all around.

"In all probability, in a few years the inhabitants of the colonies will outnumber those of Great Britain and Ireland together!"

The crowd hollered approval of this prediction.

"Yet, we colonists, wanting mere representation in Parliament, have been branded with the odious names of traitors and rebels only for complaining of our grievances! I ask, how long should this treatment be borne?"

Hollers of disapproval.

"I ask Massachusetts Governor Francis Bernard and Lieutenant Governor and Chief Justice Thomas Hutchinson to take a stand with us against such onerous behavior from our King and Parliament," Adams said, his voice waning from the high pitch of moments before.

"They must understand—we all must understand that this tea business that began May tenth is simply one more brick piled upon a foundation of ill treatment of the Commonwealth of Massachusetts and, yes, of all the American colonies. It sends us the same message—the message that, in the eyes of Lord North and King George the Third, we're second-class British citizens. Second-class citizens with no right to representation in the hallowed halls of Westminster. They consider us feeble cousins unworthy of equality!"

Jeers rang around the buildings of the street. *Oh, if I could speak like this!* Francis thought.

Adams continued: "Earlier this month, Philadelphia formed a committee in opposition to the tea tax and the monopoly of the East India Company and forced British tea agents to resign their positions. In November, I will call on our town meeting here in Boston to endorse Philadelphia's actions."

The people hailed this announcement. Their anger was boiling over. They could hardly contain themselves. They jeered King George and Lord North. Calls for "representation" filled the icy air. A bitter wind from the harbor began to slip around the buildings and down the streets. Francis felt it, tugged his cloak closer about his body and saw into the future. He saw the rightness of the Americans' response. He had heard this type of talk before—from James Otis and others of the Sons of Liberty. He now saw the earnest bitterness seething within the hearts of the people around him. He saw the probability of revolution take one more step toward reality. And he saw the possibility of victory—remote as it may seem since the colonists were ill-equipped, ill-prepared, ill-provisioned and untrained for any type of revolution against what was certainly the most powerful government on earth—France or no France.

Francis walked briskly from the crowd. He had a sermon to give in a couple of hours, and there couldn't be any anger or bitterness in his spirit when he spoke. He was well aware he was a useless lump of coal unless he was totally possessed of God. He thought of the Apostle Paul's admonition to Timothy: "No soldier when in service gets entangled in the enterprises of civilian life; his aim is to satisfy and please the One who enlisted him."

When Jesus walked on the earth, the Roman government controlled the land of Israel with a stern hand—far more stern than the British ruled the American colonies. And yet He never preached rebellion. In fact, His only mention of the Roman government was to "give unto Caesar what is Caesar's" when He spoke of paying taxes.

Jesus didn't mix politics with religion. If He had done so, He would have made it nearly impossible to preach to one entire group of people.

Francis had to determine whether he sided with John Adams and his colleagues who were on the verge of calling for revolution, or his homeland, which was clearly pressing a heavy hand upon the necks of the colonists. He couldn't voice a dissent that would lead to British charges of tyranny. Yet he would not distance himself from the colonists, whose hearts he mightily wanted to win.

Help me, Lord, to be a "good soldier," involved in the affairs of the kingdom of God rather than this earthly kingdom in which I am simply a sojourner, he prayed. *Help me to stay committed to winning souls.*

Even as he prayed, he knew times of turmoil awaited him and his colleagues as well as all the colonists and the British. There certainly were colonists with kin in the British military. If there were to be a war, would brother make the life-and-death decision to fight brother? Would cousin fight cousin? Most colonists immigrated from England, yet they would be firing bullets at their own countrymen. Would a revolution prove blood *not* to be thicker than water?

The Bible prompted him to pray for his leaders, but which leaders—colonial or parliamentary?

He decided to pray for both colonial and British statesmen and legislators—for wisdom, righteousness and forgiveness. But at the same time, he sensed that the tearing that had begun between the American colonists and the British was irreparable. And he also felt that the colonists, being in the right, would have the favor of the Almighty in any impending battle.

CHAPTER 4

Revolution!

As time passed and ill feelings festered, Francis' sentiments had tilted more and more to the side of the maligned colonists.

In 1774 a convention representing every town and district in the Massachusetts County of Suffolk, led by Doctor Joseph Warren, unanimously approved a resolution that on one hand asserted allegiance to King George the Third, but on the other prepared for war. The resolution declared: "The power but not the justice, the vengeance but not the wisdom of Great Britain, which of old persecuted, scourged, and exiled our fugitive parents from their native shores, now pursues us, their guiltless children, with unrelenting severity."

The piercing words did not grow more tender as the declaration continued. The delegation spelled out injury after injury perpetrated upon the colonies by the British Parliament. They charged the British with protecting vicious criminals from facing trial, appointing unqualified justices, ransacking the pockets of the colonists, perverting the law in gross infractions against them, and establishing the Roman Catholic religion in nearby Canada, which they declared "is dangerous in an extreme degree to the Protestant religion and to the civil rights and liberties of all America."

Least of the offenses was blocking up Boston Harbor, which the colonists of Suffolk County considered one more step endangering them. Not only were the streets of Boston "thronged with military executioners," the resolution declared that fortifications being built upon Boston Neck were "alarming to this county, and give us reason to apprehend some hostile intention against that town...."

For their own protection and that of their future generations, the Americans said they would merely act defensively. This included recommending that those holding commissions be elected in each town as officers in the militia, and that inhabitants of those towns and districts who were qualified work diligently "to acquaint themselves with the art of war."

Suffolk full-heartedly proclaimed that until its rights were fully restored, it would recommend that other counties also withhold all commercial intercourse with Great Britain, Ireland, and the West Indies, and boycott British merchandise.

These pronouncements frightened the clergy, and divided them as well.

Francis had not won many friends among his colleagues, that was certain. Neither Boardman nor Thomas Rankin, who had come to replace Boardman and rule the Methodists for John Wesley, cared to listen to Francis' pleas for a circuit-riding preacher. Indeed, soon there would be none outside Francis himself.

In early 1775, by letter, Rankin howled against the Americans and their "wicked revolt" against England. He even persuaded Wesley to call for all Methodist ministers to return to England. The other denominations had done the same. A mass exodus of preachers followed from the New World. If there were to be war, they would not be caught in the middle of it. But Francis would have none of that. There were lost souls, and those souls did not reside only in Philadelphia, New York City and Boston!

Early on, Wesley had indeed supported the call of certain Americans for independence. But when he changed his tune, Francis was livid. He accompanied Richard Wright to the ship on which Wright was sailing home from Philadelphia. At the gangplank, they both tried to persuade the other to their point of view.

"Frankie, John Wesley is our leader," Richard said, "and he has ordered us home."

"Right now, my 'home' is here," Francis said. "And I am truly sorry that that venerable man ever dipped into the politics of America. For me, this revolution is simply an unfortunate interruption in our primary concern, Richard, and that is the extension of Christ to the New World. With people keyed up about tea taxes and British raids and military musters, they're too heated up to attend to preaching, or hearing the Word of God preached."

"All the more reason to return home." Richard caught himself. "I mean to England."

"I believe that, for me, it would be an eternal disgrace to forsake—in their time of trouble—the thousands of poor sheep in the wilderness who have placed themselves under our care," Francis said, frustrated that Richard could not see the logic of his argument. "Besides, I fully sympathize with their cause and intend to show my resolve for them by sharing in their sufferings. If this infant country fails, then I will uphold them in their failure. If they prevail, then whoever remains will have won their favor by standing with them!"

Richard decided to try another angle.

"Your original plan was to return home after four years, Frankie, and it's been almost four years. Don't you want to see your parents, Emily, your friends?"

The mention of his parents, and of Emily, stung Francis. It pierced his heart. He had recently received a letter from her and she was thrilled at the thought of his coming home. She still was waiting for him, but it couldn't be. And he had struggled sleeplessly over the loss of the girl who would have been his wife, if he had only asked for her hand. He could not ask her then for marriage—for reasons that still existed today.

And his parents? He wrote letter after letter to them, longed to hold his mother in his arms, to take a long walk with his father to seek his wisdom and advice. But, no! His work was here, in the colonies. And when he did leave, it could not be in the middle of turmoil or revolution.

"Frankie, by staying, you yourself will become a rebel—if not against England then against the church!" Richard pleaded as a sudden mass of travelers pushed their way by him. "The colonists will insist you sign an oath disclaiming allegiance to England, and perhaps even enlist you into the Revolutionary Army."

"I'll have to leave that in God's hands. Besides, these are the people who need us, Richard. They're distressed above measure at the thought of being forsaken by the preachers. They need us so much more than England. England has John and Charles Wesley, George Whitfield, Jane Cooper, Philip Embury, Barbara Heck, Thomas Webb—Pilmore has returned there. When your ship arrives, Richard, they'll have nearly every British preacher alive today! And think on this: Christ's realm is more important than England's, and my primary loyalty is to Christ, who is neither English nor American. Is He?"

Richard simply shook his head in frustration that his best friend could not agree to his point of view, an opinion shared by the Wesleys and almost every other preacher on both sides of the ocean. And now, if he were to stay longer, Francis might persuade him, too.

For his part, Francis' exasperation felt like steam shut up in a teakettle. When the foremast of Wright's ship disappeared from sight, Francis still stood at the wharf, watching, motionless. Only a handful of missionaries remained in America and Francis was the only Methodist.

I, only I, am left, he thought. For a moment a touch of despair tried to wriggle into his emotions. But he quickly dispelled it, thinking of Gideon's army and how God, to prove His almighty power, whittled Gideon's forces down to a precious few before bringing a great victory against overwhelming odds.

He turned slowly to look about him. To the south, he knew the mainland stretched for a thousand miles, beyond Virginia and the Carolinas, beyond Georgia's rice paddies and sugar plantations. Ironic, wasn't it, that Georgia was named for King George III, the very Sovereign against whom the colonies were going to war?

To the north, it stretched another thousand miles to the shipyards and cornfields of Massachusetts and the frontier territory of Maine. Would John Winthrop and the others who founded the colony one hundred and forty-five years before turn over in their graves at the thought of this rebellion?

And what of his own thoughts? If he had spoken against King George, he would be cut loose from his colleagues in England. If he spoke against the colonies, he could not continue his work in America. If King George knew of him, he probably thought of Francis as disloyal to the Crown. If George Washington knew of him, he probably thought he should have been more vocally supportive of the Revolution. On the one hand, he refused to renounce his British citizenship; on the other, he must avoid being drafted, for that would block any attempt at evangelism. As always, foremost on his mind was that his primary loyalty was to the risen Christ, the One Who changed men's hearts regardless of their nationality, and Who, indeed, was neither American nor British.

Francis knew that some would refuse to consider him impartial and would instead deem him an enemy, an adversary to seize and violently abuse.

•••••

Several days later, Francis was lunching with some members of a Methodist church he had established in the village of Aberdeen in Maryland. They were dining at the home of Methodist trustee, Joseph Presbury, and his wife, Elinor. He was sitting at one end of a large table, with five couples—a handful of children gathered around a smaller table nearby—and they were engrossed in a discussion of Jonah and the whale.

"It wasn't even a whale; it was a 'large fish,'" said Bob Towson, sitting at the opposite end of the table.

"Whichever it was, it must have smelled beyond horrible in the creature's stomach," sniffed Kate Cornwald. "Imagine!"

"And for three days!" added Annabelle Knowland, wrinkling her nose.

Francis simply watched, listened and smiled, his elbows resting on the edge of the table, his hands folded together in front of him. The lunch had been scrumptious, especially satisfying since so many of his meals were smoked or salted fish or meat eaten beside a campfire, or no fire at all.

"I don't know that this even happened," declared Joshua Smith. "A fish swallowing a man?"

"Maybe Jonah was a very small man," smiled Joseph. Everyone laughed.

"Perhaps the story is all an allegory," said Betsy Towson.

"Perhaps it was a Hebrew fable passed down through the generations, to warn us to obey God or else," offered Seth Crawford. He turned with a questioning look toward Francis and the entire table followed his gaze.

"An allegory? A fable?" Francis asked. He shook his head and looked around the table. "If you think so, you will have a problem with Christ Himself."

Betsy, Seth and several of the others recoiled, as if pushed backward, taken aback at the implication. Their looks implored Francis to continue.

"Jesus actually prophesied that He would experience something similar to Jonah," Francis said. "In Matthew chapter twelve, verse forty, He said, 'For as Jonah was three days and three nights in the belly of a huge fish, so the Son of Man will be three days and three nights in the heart of the earth'."

Comments of assent came from around the table.

Francis asked, "So Jesus obviously did not think the story of Jonah and the big fish an allegory or fable, did He?"

Like pupils in a classroom, they shook their heads.

"The similarities don't end there," Francis continued. "God sent Jonah to save a perverse non-Jewish city, Nineveh, which was ripe for judgment. He sent Jesus—who, by the way, we should really be calling by His Hebrew name *Yeshua*—to spread the good news of salvation to sinful mankind, the Jew and the Gentile alike."

He looked down the table. "Joseph, you're a student of Hebrew."

Joseph nodded.

"Do you know what Jonah's name means?"

Joseph thought for a moment. "Is it 'dove'?"

"Very good," Francis said. "Doves in the Bible are usually associated with good news. After the flood, a dove revealed that the water had receded. When Jesus was baptized, the Holy Spirit descended on Him like a dove, affirming that He was the Son of God.

"But …" Francis held up his forefinger, "Hosea says in the seventh chapter that a dove is 'easily deceived and senseless.' So we must determine what kind of 'dove' Jonah was—a messenger of good news or a silly bird, eh?" Francis turned his forefinger and middle finger into a bird flying helter-skelter.

Light laughter met the antics.

Francis continued, "When told by his Creator to go to Tarshish, what does Jonah do?"

"Run!" Betsy responded.

"Correct. So God had to get his attention, right?"

Betsy nodded. "He certainly did!"

"In no uncertain way. In the midst of a horrendous storm, Jonah confesses to the ship's crew that the Creator is after him, which leads them to toss him overboard as a sacrifice to satisfy God. But—" Again, Francis raised his forefinger, "but God directed a huge fish to swallow him up, saving him from drowning. Yet he remained a stubborn man, I would say, wouldn't you?"

Questioning looks met his eyes.

"It took him three days in the belly of this 'stinky fish'—" he smiled at Kate and Annabelle, "before he called out to God. Three days!"

People shook their heads at the thought of the arduous time.

"This story of Jonah teaches us several things about God," Francis said. "He is patient. He is powerful. There is no end He will not go to in order to reach out to us—even to the point of changing the course of nature to get Jonah's attention.

"But, perhaps most of all, this story shows us that God is forgiving. He was so concerned for the salvation of the hundred and twenty thousand people of Nineveh—and these were wicked, violent people—that He sent a man who was completely opposed to it, and to the people of Nineveh, to preach repentance to them."

"And they received his message and repented," said Joseph.

"Yes, and later fell back into their old sins," Joshua added.

"True, Joshua," Francis said, "but God's door is always open to the repentant right up until one's final breath. Jesus remains the perfect sacrifice, once for all time, Jew and Gentile alike."

Bob leaned forward, his brow knitted in seriousness. "Reverend Asbury, do you feel that the pastors who boarded ships back to England and Europe were like Jonah? Did they flee from the duties to which God had called them?"

Francis was stunned by the comparison. He reached for the cup of tea before him and took a sip. He could not condemn these men, but—they were misguided, misdirected, not listening to the Holy Spirit of God, but—in hesitation, he took another sip and thought over the question for another moment.

Finally, he fixed his gaze on the handsome young man before him.

"You know better than I, Bob, that these are difficult times. For all of us here and all of those in England. Add a measure of fear to these men's bent toward submission to authority and you find very good reasons to act as they did."

Francis felt a sermon coming on, but stopped himself. These were good men he was considering, all of them in a strange new world, many of them called to do things for which they were unpracticed. He laughed for a moment at the thought of one colleague, fresh off the ship from England, stepping up onto the saddle for the first time and urging the horse to move forward. "Proceed!" he called, but the animal did not know his vocabulary!

Francis looked down the table at this group of noble pioneers— all of them people whose ancestors, or they themselves, had come to the colonies, leaving their old lives behind and forging new lives. Here he was, with the opportunity to share with them and three million like them in America, the "new life" that Christ offered them. He knew how they would have felt had he, too, joined the other preachers on a voyage back across the Atlantic.

Again looking directly at Bob, he resumed: "I can judge no man in reference to whether he has done what God has called him to do. I can only answer for myself, and I *would have* felt like Jonah if I had left, also. I *would have* known that I had violated God's plan for me. I *would have* been constantly looking over my shoulder thinking God was chasing me and at the same time anxious that He would never want to try to use me again.

"Jonah was truly fortunate that the Lord didn't just let him sail away to who-knows-where and use someone else to prophesy to Nineveh. His entire eternity would have been squandered."

•••••

Two days later, Francis was riding southward alongside the east bank of the Pokomoke River in Delaware. It was a damp day following a drizzly night in which he had slept cuddled up to the belly of his horse, Silver Fox. No settlement was in sight and the dampness had made it impossible to start a fire when darkness descended upon them the previous evening. Silver Fox had been a perfect lady as he cozied up to feel her body warmth, never kicking or squirming, somehow knowing that he was depending on her for heat and shelter.

Now, here it was mid-morning, his four hours of Bible-reading were behind him, and they were on their way to Annapolis, where he intended to preach that night. That is, if the authorities would allow it. He had heard that two preachers, Joseph Hartley and Freeborn Garrettson, had been imprisoned for not taking an oath in support of the colonies. He must get to his destination, but avoid any patrols of the Continental Army, or he might end up in the same predicament. To say the least, this war was an unfortunate interruption in soul-winning!

Francis wrapped his longcoat tight about him as Silver Fox trotted on, drops of water falling off the brim of his hat. He was praying silently—for he knew the devil would let him read always rather than pray. Many matters weighed on his mind, but especially his mother, even more than this war. He had received a letter from his father that she was ill and he prayed desperately that God would heal her.

Suddenly, he heard the sounds of at least several horses up ahead on the trail. Quickly, quietly, he turned Silver Fox toward a heavy thicket of evergreen trees and retreated behind them just as a half-dozen men rode by, two wide and three deep. On the left front, a rough-looking character was speaking to the man beside him. "If Asbury is speaking tonight at Gumboro he'll be passing this way, Davey. We grab him, get him to sign an oath to America, denounce England, and he can be on his way. If not, we jail him. No question about it."

"And you think one of the patrols'll find him on this trail, Jake?"

"Either us, or one of the others. Preferably us, though, eh, Davey?" Jake winked at his compatriot. "Have a little fun with a preacher-man?"

Davey gave a quirky, crooked, half-smile in response.

Francis didn't like the looks, nor the attitude, of these men. He stroked Silver Fox along her cheek and sh-h-h'd in her ear. "Be invisible, fine lady," he whispered and backed her up to be better hidden as these men passed by a dozen yards away.

He realized that he also had to watch out for other patrols, according to this Jake fellow. When the men were out of earshot, Francis quietly turned Silver Fox eastward. A few minutes later he was in a swamp. At first the water was a few inches high, then knee-high, and then waist-high, so that it reached his stirrups. It was hard, mucky going for Silver Fox. If Francis had felt he could walk through it himself, he would have dismounted; but visions of getting forever stuck in this place nixed that idea.

Did this swamp never end? He feared that it would lead him right into the ocean. But he feared even more that, if he went back to the path, he would be taken prisoner.

Francis prayed for a dry sky, but even more for dry land. *Lord, You gave Jonah a plant to shade him, if even for a little while! Dry ground. Is there any around?*

Seconds later, scanning the seemingly endless swamp—which he later found out to be called the Great Pocomoke Swamp, and "great" for good reason since it covered 173 square miles—he noticed a tiny little elevation of land, anchored by a beech tree, to the south. When Francis and Silver Fox arrived at the spot, he jumped down from the horse to allow her to climb onto the little bit of ground. It was perhaps three yards square. The swamp water had nearly reached his saddlebag, but not quite. Reaching into it, he pulled out a bag of sugar cubes and placed one in his outstretched palm to reward Silver Fox. She licked it from his hand, then nuzzled him with an accompanying whinny.

Pungent smells like that of mold and dirty rags constantly wafted around the swamp—an odor as real a presence as if it had two hands and two feet. Francis and Silver Fox stayed their ground, anxious to move on. But Francis possessed an ominous feeling that he must remain there.

Day turned into night and then day again. Francis looked up through the branches of the tree to the sky, which was entirely gray except for one small circle about twenty-five to thirty degrees above the horizon. In that circle the blue sky beyond was clear.

Isaiah chapter 51:6 occurred to him: *"Lift up your eyes to the heavens, look at the earth beneath; the heavens will vanish like smoke, the earth will wear out like a garment, and its inhabitants die like flies. But My salvation will last forever, My righteousness will never fail."*

The Holy Spirit spoke to Francis: "Son, no matter how disheartening the signs, how distressing the actions of those around you; no matter the depression that wants to weigh heavily upon your heart, declaring that all is gray and lost—no matter all this: I am here with you. You merely have to look in the right place, not at the appearances of the world but to Him Who delivers from the darkness.

"Keep your eyes looking heavenward on the Deliverer, not the depressor. And that Deliverer will be there to direct your walk and be a beacon shining out of the grayness in your circumstances."

Francis prayed: *Oh, Father, I too often look only at the physical around me and feel overwhelmed, not searching out where You sit, watching over me with compassion and a steady hand of deliverance. Thank You for being ever present. Amen.*

And day turned to night and then day again, and yet Francis remained on his little piece of land, observing the creation all about him while Silver Fox was clearly anxious to go—somewhere, anywhere.

At mid-morning on the third day, Francis mounted Silver Fox, reached up to snap a leaf-laden branch from the tree, then got off the horse and fed it to her. Looking skyward, he said, "Thank You, Lord, for Your provision." Turning to Silver Fox, he asked, "Right, girl? Part of that tree died for your nourishment, like the Savior died so that men might live."

Francis pulled a couple of pieces of beef jerky from his saddle bag, gave one piece to Silver Fox and sat down to chew the other piece.

As he sat, he noticed a pair of pileated woodpeckers hammering away at a beech tree. Now this tree looked like the least likely candidate to serve up a daily treat of bugs—especially for birds of this huge size. How could there be any bugs inside this healthy specimen? *There are certainly less healthy-looking trees immediately around it*, he thought, scanning the trees interspersed on tufts of earth around the swamp. Yet these woodpeckers were coming to this one beech tree and apparently had found a gold mine.

Francis contemplated the scene in light of the world he had encountered. *We may look free of spiritual "bugs" and may fool the world about how "healthy" we are*, he thought, *but if there is anything amiss inside us—any pest eating away at our souls—it will be found out. And when it is, the process of extricating it from within us is bound to be painful. Ouch!*

"Psalm forty-one tells us that God knows the secrets of the heart," Francis said to Silver Fox while patting her regal nose. "Lord, help me to remove any dangerous 'pests' within me before any outside force comes to do so. Purify me, O Lord. Purify me!"

And again, day turned into night and then day again. Francis awoke to the snort of his horse. He was leaning back against the tree and Silver Fox was standing. Her ears were straight up, rotating as if on a swivel, first to the left and then the right.

"Do you hear something, girl?" Francis asked, pushing himself to a standing position and peering in the direction she looked. Silver Fox snorted again and leaned down, settling her giant head up against his chest.

Apparently the morning passed Silver Fox's smell test. Thinking of smell, Francis noticed that the nasty smell of the swamp no longer bothered him. He had become used to it. He looked heavenward, realizing he had completed three days on this tiny spot of land, isolated from the world.

"Lord, I give a little teaching on Jonah and You make me live three days and three nights in the middle of my own whale—this, this swamp! Is this 'humor' You're showing me here?"

He could only smile as the Spirit of God taught him. *Francis, I wanted you to see the lost for who they are, what spiritual condition they are in. I wanted you to see that you cannot expect them to act as if they are saved. They are not. Do you smell the swamp now?*

"No. Not like before, on the first day," he said aloud.

Correct. Because you have lived in this place, you cannot smell the decay. Think of the people in the wilderness of these colonies—and even in the towns and cities. Many have lived not just days, but years, decades in the "smell" of their sins. They are used to those sins, so those sins do not hold a nasty odor for them anymore.

"I see that, Lord," Francis said.

And so you see that once they do know Me, the stench of those sins will be too much for them to bear—

"Yes, Lord!"

Good. Then you can leave this place now. The American troops will not find you.

A couple of hours later, emerging from the swamp, Francis turned Silver Fox westward, to ford the Pokomoke River and make his way to Baltimore, Maryland, deciding Gumboro would have to wait.

•••••

"Yuck! A smelly swamp!" young Thomas piped up when Francis told of the Great Pokomoke. "And weren't you hungry after three days, Bishop?"

Francis smiled down at the boy. "Beef jerky can satisfy you only so long, Thomas. That's all I had in my saddlebag. And a canteen of water, thank God."

"So, you had to hide for the rest of the Revolution?" Sam asked.

"Well, for a year or longer. It was a difficult time," Francis said. "I stayed with families from Boston to Richmond, Virginia, trying to avoid the authorities, but at the same time making it clear that I supported the Colonies in the Revolution. I simply couldn't take up arms. The only weapon I'm familiar with is the Word of God. That's my sword. Instead of taking lives, I wanted to save them."

"How long did you have to hide out?" asked Reverend Matthews.

"Quite a while. Then, in March of seventeen-hundred-and-seventy-eight I retired to Delaware, to the house of my good friend, Judge Thomas White, for ten months. Thank God for that venerable man and his sweet wife, Nellie! They placed themselves in severe danger—for they would have reaped the consequences if I were caught. Nevertheless, they even pressed me to preach in their home, or their barn, to neighbors in all directions.

"'We've just got to be careful, very careful,' the judge warned. 'I realize your belief against swearing an oath of allegiance because you feel all oaths are wrong. But others consider that belief as bordering on Loyalist sympathies.'

"Well, yes, they did," Francis continued, "but I dispelled those thoughts at every opportunity I had, and in no uncertain terms! James chapter five verse twelve says, 'Above all, my brothers, don't swear—not by heaven or by earth or by anything else. Let your "yes" be "yes" and your "no," "no," or you will be condemned.' I'd rather be condemned by men than by God."

"You never got caught preaching in the Whites' home?" asked Abigail.

"No, but I did get caught once elsewhere. I felt compelled to get to Annapolis to see how the body of Christ was doing there, but alas, that was too far to venture."

"What happened?" Abigail urged.

It was a bright, sunny day in late June, Francis recalled. He was leading the congregation, gathered in a farmer's barn, in singing a new Charles Wesley hymn. Someone was playing a fiddle and another was drumming lightly on a calf-skin fiddle. With horses and sheep joining the chorus every several seconds, they sang:

> "And can it be that I should gain an interest
> in the Savior's blood?
> Died He for me, who caused His pain?
> For me, who Him to death pursued?
> Amazing love! How can it be that Thou, my
> God, should die for me!"

Oh, how exhilarating!

> "He left His Father's throne above, so free, so
> infinite His grace!
> Emptied Himself of all but love, and bled for
> Adam's helpless race!
> Tis mercy all, immense and free, for, O my
> God, it found out me.
> Amazing love! How can it be that Thou, my
> God, shouldst die for me!"

Oh, but Brother Charles could write!

Suddenly the large barn door crashed open and five soldiers of the Continental Army stepped boldly inside. The man in the lead—supposedly an officer, it was so difficult to tell any one of them from the farmers and other townspeople gathered in the building—spoke out as he pointed at Francis. "Are you Francis Asbury?" he demanded.

Francis shrugged, "Of course."

"Then you're preaching illegally, sir!"

Several of the men in the barn began to demand that the intruders leave the barn. Two men of the congregation stepped in front of Francis to protect him.

Francis held up his hand to silence everyone.

"How can one preach illegally?" he asked.

"Have you sworn the oath?" the officer demanded, a snarl curling his lip.

"I don't swear," Francis replied, "either by the heavens, which is God's throne room, nor by the earth, which is His footstool. I swear not! But my 'yes' will be 'yes' and my 'no,' 'no,' sir." His blue eyes pierced the man before him. "I affirm your struggle against England. Indeed, I support either of the seals proposed for this new nation put forth by Mister Franklin and Mister Jefferson—Mister Franklin's showing Moses dividing the Red Sea and Mister Jefferson's representation of the Israelites being led in the wilderness by the pillar of fire by night and the cloud by day. And I favor the proposed motto, 'Rebellion to tyrants is obedience to God.' But I will never raise a hand in anger—against either side in this Revolution."

The soldier was unaffected. "With no oath, you stand fined five pounds, Mister Asbury." He took one step forward, extending the palm of his hand. "And I'll have that money now, or to jail you'll go!"

"Five pounds! That's a king's ransom!"

"Yes, and the King has been holding us up to ransom for years now, hasn't he?"

"What have I to do with the King? And who has five pounds?"

"You'll have it, or you'll be behind bars this day, sir!"

Francis threw up his hands. "Then to jail I go. Only let me take my Bible with me." As he reached for his Bible on a table, one of the men who had stood before him, Ronald Jones, called out, "Five pounds? Have we not five pounds among us here?"

Everyone in the barn, perhaps forty in all, scrambled for

their pockets. Ronald walked around the barn, holding his hat high. Coins were tossed into it from all sides as he made his way clockwise around the building. Once, when he slowed his step, a large bay horse leaned out of his stall and nudged him, nearly knocking him over, and everyone in the barn laughed. Even the soldier in charge had a difficult time submerging a chuckle.

Finally, Ronald finished the offering and counted out the money. "One pound. Two pounds. Two pounds five. Three pounds. Three pounds six. Four pounds. Four pounds five, seven, eight...."

Ronald looked up, puzzlement and disappointment etched on his face. "We're twenty pence short," he said softly.

As men around the barn turned their money pouches inside out looking for another coin, one of the Army patrol, a skinny young fellow, stepped over to Ronald's hat and tossed in a coin.

"Higgins!" screamed the soldier in charge. "What are ya doing?"

"Why, topping off the collection, Sir," the young man replied. A round of applause from the entire congregation greeted the announcement. Francis looked at the lad and smiled. *God has His hand on this boy*, he thought.

"Top off the collection!? We came here to arrest this man for preachin'— and you give toward his fine!"

Higgins began to cower, but then felt better of it and straightened his shoulders. "Yes, Sir. And proud of it, I am, Sir!"

"We'll see if you remain proud of it, Private!" With that, the soldier in charge turned to Ronald. "I'll take that money." Looking at Francis, he declared, "You're a marked man in these parts, Parson."

"I can only pray that wouldn't be," Francis replied.

"No more preachin' for you, Sir."

Francis simply bowed his head. He would not agree to any such demand.

This began an even more difficult two years for Francis at Judge White's. He went into hiding and showed himself only to preach. He felt like a mole, stuck in the dark. Agh-h! The thought of it, even years later, made him squirm. Imagine! Not able to ride freely through the colonies. Contained by four walls during daylight hours, only able to leave in the nighttime quietly to visit the settlements.

"Dumb, silent Sabbaths—," Francis said, turning to Robert Matthews. "Dumb, silent Sabbaths! It was torture. Staying exiled like a criminal, holed up, unable to preach but once or twice a week. It drove me to distraction.

"And then, even the judge, who promised me security and secrecy, was himself taken into custody by the light-horse patrol; and I wondered, if such a thing could happen to him, a judge, what might I expect—a fugitive, and an Englishman?"

•••••

"But there were victories....," Robert stated.

"Oh, yes! My favorite story of salvation—ever." Francis looked about the room. "Do you remember the famous Doctor Thomas Hinde?"

"Yes," Robert said. "From Kentucky. I've met him at a couple of national Methodist conferences. A staunch man of God. A funny fellow. Wonderful sense of humor."

"Yes, but not always, and he will be the first to tell you."

Francis recalled his first meeting—call it a confrontation—with the good Doctor Hinde. It was at the Hinde estate, in a grand room where balls were danced and bands played—a room where Mrs. Elizabeth Hinde had asked him to preach.

He had not known that Doctor Hinde was not, well, amenable to the event. Especially in his own home. Especially in a time of war. Especially, Hinde thought, when it was this late-coming Englishman who was sharing this rubbish about God. God? What God?! A foolish vision, a dream to which weaklings might hold. Sentimental fluff! And his wife, Elizabeth, was being drawn into this folly! A quick dose of reality would wake all these "Christians" from their silly aspirations for eternal life. Doctor Hinde sniffed at the thought. Eternal life. Salvation. And deliverance? Deliverance from what? It was simple nature to break every single one of those

Ten Commandments. And, except for murder and adultery, who hadn't done so? The question screamed to be asked. And so he did.

Doctor Hinde entered his ballroom the moment Francis finished his closing prayer. With people Hinde had never before seen milling about—in his home, mind you!—he stomped across the floor to face this arrogant preacher.

Disregarding Elizabeth, who was asking Francis a question, Doctor Hinde declared, "Sir, I understand my wife invited you here. But, I declare, I'm most upset at this, this trivial invention you have brought into my house."

Francis turned to face the man. Doctor Hinde was taller and barrel-chested, outweighing Francis by at least fifty pounds. A full set of whiskers framed his face. And dark, dangerous-looking eyes pierced their target, Francis, with something other than affection. Francis was taken aback by the hostility emanating from this man. *If he were a water pot, it would be boiling*, Francis thought.

Finally, he responded. "Trivial invention?"

"Exactly, except that I think it not trivial to lead men and women astray with some notion of a need for this God of yours."

"You're a doctor, correct, sir?" Francis asked.

Doctor Hinde nodded.

"A scientist?"

Obviously anxious to end this inanity, Doctor Hinde said curtly, "Of course. What of it?"

"Well, as a doctor and a scientist, you deal with what is provable. Correct?"

"Yes, and you can't tell me you can prove that this God exists. I'm no nick ninny that you can bamboozle with a cock-and-bull story."

"Dear doctor, I would never think you a simpleton who can be fooled by any story at all. But would you say that other scientists operate on the same assumptions of proof?"

"Of course."

"Then you'll be happy to know that Sir Isaac Newton, the father of mathematics, was a believer in Christ—along with the father of chemistry, Sir Robert Boyle, astrologer Johann Baptist Cysat, astronomer John Flamsteed, microbiologist Anton von Leeuwenhoek and many other leaders in the world of science."

"Then they made leave of their senses," Doctor Hinde declared stiffly. "I repeat, you can not prove to me that this God exists."

"How about if I prove by the process of elimination? What if I show you that other options are less believable than the existence of a Creator? Indeed, that those options are absurd?"

"You want an exercise in futility? Then go ahead, try." Doctor Hinde folded his large arms, certain of victory but nevertheless just wanting it to be over with. He was a man whose time wasn't cheap, after all. And this, this minister of God, was occupying space in his home and with time on his clock!

"Hold out your hand, sir," Francis asked.

"What?"

"Hold out your hand, please."

Reluctantly, Doctor Hinde did so.

"Fold it into a fist."

Doctor Hinde obliged.

"Now, hit your other palm with that fist. And, if you'd like," Francis smiled, "pretend that the palm is my face."

Doctor Hinde smacked his palm with ringing force.

Francis withheld another smile. "How did you make that fist, Doctor?"

Doctor Hinde spit out, "My brain simply told my hand to make a fist, of course!"

"Simply?" Francis said. "How in the world would you have a brain that could accomplish such a feat without a Designer of that brain? How would you have such a complicated hand, with fingers that can move independently or together, that can curl and uncurl, that feel pressure and pain, that feel cold and warmth, that bend at the perfect places to make them so maneuverable, if there were not a Creator?"

Doctor Hinde looked at his hand and then at Francis, then shook off the question with a "Phshaw!"

Francis persisted. "Dear sir, you hit your palm with a peak of anger, thinking it me. Where did that irritation exist?"

"If there were irritation it would be in my mind, of course," Doctor Hinde responded.

"A simple thing, the mind, eh?" Francis said. "How in the world can a thing, a place, just happen to be—not designed by any Being or Force—that can house such things as emotions? Anger, fear, anxiety, remorse, thanksgiving—love. How can all these emotions simply—exist?"

"They—simply—exist," Doctor Hinde said. "And, sir, if there were a God, at least a God I could believe in, He would not allow sickness, pain and death—all of which I see in appalling abundance!" With that, the gentleman turned and left the room before Francis could share the story of the fall of man.

Within days, Doctor Hinde pronounced Elizabeth insane! With just the two of them in their home, he commanded her to their bed. Honoring her husband, she did so.

He then entered the room with a white ceramic bowl in hand, the type of bowl he used in his practice.

"What I have here, my dear, is mustard plaster," he said. "I am going to draw the religion out of your head!"

Elizabeth's eyes went large and she shivered in fright, but she did not get out of bed and run, she did not complain, she simply sat in the bed awaiting her fate. She prayed softly.

As Doctor Hinde began to apply the hot concoction, her prayers lifted a bit in volume. As he caked it all over her scalp, the prayers increased in speed and soared higher still. And as the heat from the plaster began to bake Elizabeth's skin, her speech turned to singing, and her English broke into a language Doctor Hinde had never heard before. It was beautiful! And when the mustard mixture began to blister her skin, Elizabeth called to her husband, "More, dear man! More that I may share the pain my Savior endured on the cross for my sins!"

She was imploring him to inflict more torture and persecution upon her! His dear Liz, the woman he had adored since they were schoolchildren together, the woman who had borne him three children and had cared for him and them like no other wife could, was happier blistered than unblistered! How could that be? How could that be—unless—unless her convictions were true, unless there was a God who could comfort her in the midst of such distress and pain?

Tears flooding down his face and into his whiskers, he quickly stood to his feet and pulled Elizabeth toward a wash pan on her vanity. Weeping, he toweled gobs of the mustard plaster from her head, then cupped water in his hands and poured it onto her scalp, exposing blisters that made him cringe.

Doctor Hinde sank to his knees. "Dear God! Dear God, forgive me! Forgive this prideful man! Forgive my savagery!

"Oh, God, Liz, what have I done?" he gasped, wiping the torrent of tears from his cheeks.

With the face of an angel, Elizabeth looked down at him and smiled. "Why, Thomas," she said softly, "I think you found God!"

•••••

"Ah, what a wonderful story," declared Sam Brackett.

"Ours is a great God, eh?" said Robert.

"Yes, he did an extraordinary work in the good doctor," Francis said. "And, ever since, he has kept an open house for us Methodist preachers and is a prominent figure in Kentucky Methodism."

"Did you ever see that soldier, Higgins, again, Bishop?" asked little Thomas.

Francis broke into a broad smile. "Thomas, you're a bright lad, remembering that boy. Yes! Somehow, Daniel—that was his Christian name—discovered that I was preaching in a neighboring grist mill a few nights after that exchange with him and the other militia in the barn. He came to hear the message and gave his heart to Christ that very night. I see him whenever I preach in those parts, raising his hands to the Lord in worship. He has a beautiful wife and two children—both of them all grown up now and all of them wholly given to the Lord."

"See how God multiplies!" Sam said. "And how he turns bad

to good? He turned the evil intent of man that night in the barn, into a turning point in the life of Higgins and even the generation that followed."

"Well, Bishop," Robert said, "I hate to break this up, but you have another message to give in an hour."

Francis nodded. He was expectant of a move of God. Someone tonight would be saved. A sinner would be turned from his ways. Francis could feel it in his spirit and it added fuel to the fire of his heart. *One more soul, Lord! One more soul for the kingdom!*

CHAPTER 5

War-bound

Arriving back at the Brackett home several hours later, after the evening service, everyone was in high spirits. A dozen people had gone forward to give their hearts to the Lord, including Harvey Smith, the town's blacksmith and acknowledged curmudgeon—a man everyone thought devoid of affection. As a matter of fact, he had always declared affection to being an affliction—an attitude needing adjustment, as with a sledgehammer!

"Grace finally—finally drags Harvey to church," Sam Brackett was saying, "and look what happens! Unbelievable!"

"I'll wager he didn't get on his knees when he asked Grace to marry him," Abigail laughed, "and there he was—at the altar, on his knees."

"That was a dark heart in which God's light shone, eh?" said Nicholas.

Taking everyone's coat, Sam agreed, "Darker than inside a woodshed on a moonless, starless night."

"Dark as pitch!" little Thomas said firmly. Everyone laughed.

Sam looked at Nicholas and shrugged. "One of my sayings the boy has picked up."

"He's locked Grace out of the house more than once when she has gone to church at night," Abigail offered as she walked to the stove and put a kettle of water on to heat. "Once he locked her out in the dead of winter with snow and freezing rain pelting down upon her. But I've never heard Grace complain. She never sought reprisal, always simply continued to love that man. We'd all shake our heads in wonderment, but she obviously saw something deep within him that no one else seems to have observed."

"Scripture says that even we don't know our own hearts," Francis said, lowering himself into a chair before the fireplace. "Harvey Smith didn't know his own heart. He perhaps thought he did and knew it was filled to overflowing with hardness. Compassion? Love? Forgiveness? Joy? Kindness? Patience? Harvey didn't know his heart contained any of these, and neither did we. Did we?"

Francis looked around the room. Everyone was shaking their heads. No, they didn't.

"No, but God did. He had created Harvey. He knew there was a softness beneath that tough shell that Harvey projected. Even when Harvey cursed Him, He knew. Even when Harvey's temper rose to a fit, He knew."

"But your sermon awoke that in him," Nicholas put in.

"God's Word," Francis corrected. "It's His power, not mine. Harvey didn't even know he needed salvation—until he heard the Word. He simply had to have someone share that Word with him. Once that was in his noggin," Francis playfully tapped Thomas on his head, "then he realized he could be visiting the hottest part of hell upon his death—unless he renounced that evil in his heart."

Francis, who had removed his coat and hung it on a peg beside the door, placed his hat on Thomas' head. Thomas smiled up at him, then, with seriousness etched on his little face, asked, "Why did God create evil?"

Francis pulled the boy up onto his lap. "Thomas, God did not create evil. But He did create the potential for evil. And, think of this now, without that potential for evil, love would lose its meaning."

Thomas looked blankly at Francis. To him, grasping that idea was like trying to grab smoke from a fire.

"What I'm saying, Thomas, is that God gave us free will. That is, we can do what we choose, completely disregarding what we know God wants us to do. And because of that free will, there is a potential for evil. God is not a dictator or potentate who commands us to obey Him at all costs. Obedience by fear is not an expression of love, but terror. God doesn't want that."

Thomas was still confused.

"Thomas," Francis continued, "when your Daddy asks you to do something, say bring in a stick of wood for the fire, do you obey him?"

"Why, yes, of course!" Thomas said, wide-eyed.

"Why do you obey him?"

"Because he's my Dad." Thomas smiled broadly.

"Is that all?"

Thomas thought a couple of seconds, then answered, "And I love him."

Francis nodded. "So, because he's your Dad and you love him, you obey him."

"Yes," Thomas said, then crossed his arms and added, "and 'cause he's the boss!" He looked up at his father, who had settled into another chair, and smiled.

Francis ruffled Thomas' curly hair and laughed. "All right, Thomas, have you ever *not* done what your Daddy asked you to do?"

Thomas put his fist to his chin and thought deeply, his forehead furrowing.

Abigail laughed, "So, you obey your father perfectly, Thomas? How about your mother?"

Thomas looked at his mother and bit his lower lip. "No, ma'am."

Abigail pushed on. "When your Mother tells you to stay away from the river because it's flowing so fast it's dangerous, do you always obey her?"

Thomas lowered his eyes. "No, ma'am."

"Will you obey me now—after you almost drowned last week?"

"Yes, Mother, I will!" Thomas looked up at her with the renewed vigor of a boy who is convinced he has been saved from death and is lucky to have more breaths to breathe.

"Our rules are for your own good, you know, Thomas," Sam said.

"That's true with God's commandments as well," Nicholas said. "He didn't write the Ten Commandments because He wanted to constrain our actions, but because He wanted to protect us. Go through them one by one. If we don't go after other gods and worship idols, we're saved from hell. If we don't steal or kill, we don't have to pay with the retribution of others."

"And, if we honor our father and mother, Thomas," Francis smiled at the boy, "we'll be blessed!"

"So, now, do you understand the answer to your question about God creating evil?" Sam asked his son.

Thomas nodded, pursing his lips as if very mature thoughts were running through his young mind.

The teakettle began a piercing whistle and Abigail asked, "Tea, everyone?" She received nods all around.

"Even me, Mother, please?" Thomas piped up.

"Yes, even you, child." Abigail busied herself with pouring tea from a pewter teapot into empty cups. Francis was always a bit surprised to see families that had managed to bring fragile things like tea cups and teapots and tea cozies all the way to America—and then keep them from breaking or denting. A smooth road over which to transport goods simply did not exist, and this was, after all, the wilderness. A settled town, yes, but a wilderness nonetheless.

•••••

"Francis," Sam said, "would you feel like continuing your story? You have eight ears intent on hearing it."

Francis nodded. "Surely. Where'd we leave off?"

"That doctor who plastered mustard on his wife!" Thomas declared.

"Ah, Thomas, but you're a good bookmark, aren't you, son?"

"Bookmark?"

"Something that keeps your place in a book," Sam answered. "Yes, Francis, you were talking about the American Revolution."

"Oh, that was a dangerous time!" Francis said, and the hair on his neck rose as he recalled the horrors.

In March 1778 the British Parliament sent a Peace Commission to negotiate with the colonists in Philadelphia, offering to grant all the American demands except independence. Congress rejected the offer.

Two months later, General Henry Clinton replaced General Howe as commander of all British forces in the American colonies and war turned to terror. Three hundred Iroquois Indians burned Cobleskill, New York, and then, in July, British Loyalists and Indians massacred settlers in the Wyoming Valley of northern Pennsylvania.

Clinton troops battled George Washington's forces, ending in a standoff in the bloody Battle of Monmouth in New Jersey.

In 1779, American troops from North Carolina and Virginia attacked Chickamauga Indian villages in Tennessee in retaliation for Indian raids on colonial settlements. Then British troops burned Portsmouth and Norfolk, Virginia; and Loyalists raided coastal towns in Connecticut, burning Fairfield, Norwalk, and ships in New Haven harbor.

Matters didn't improve as British and American forces crisscrossed the colonies in horrendous battles for three more years, while terror followed terror in inhuman acts: American militiamen, in March 1782, massacred ninety-six Delaware Indians in Ohio in retaliation for Indian raids conducted by other tribes; Loyalist and Indian forces, in August 1782, attacked and defeated American settlers near Lexington, Kentucky; days later, Mohawk Indian Chief Joseph Brant led raids on settlements in Pennsylvania and Kentucky; and, in November, the final battle of the Revolutionary War, Americans retaliated against Loyalist and Indian forces by attacking a Shawnee Indian village in the Ohio territory.

Through this all, Francis waged a one-man war for men's souls, trying his best to avoid armies from both sides of the conflict.

He was teaching himself Hebrew and, while studying the scriptures one day, discovered that in Judges 6:34, when the Spirit of the Lord came upon Gideon before he blew the trumpet prior to the battle with the Abiezrites, the full meaning of the Hebrew meant that God covered Gideon with Himself and took over his body. So, in dangerous circumstances, Francis asked the Lord to do the same with him.

He survived more nights in swamps, hiding out under straw in abandoned barns, and fighting off armies of fleas in pioneer shacks along the Atlantic Coast. Sometime in 1778, Delaware Governor Caesar Rodney gave Francis a passport and letters to influential men on his behalf.

Finally, all the colonial military authorities and political leaders were secure in their knowledge that Francis' sympathies were with the Americans.

Freedom!

Even though Francis had been holed up most of the time in Judge White's house, he figured eighteen hundred souls had come to the Lord during those two years, praise His Name. He wrote to Wesley in England detailing the change in his situation, and new missionaries began to trickle back into America in the 1780s, so that by war's end in 1783 eighty-three itinerant Methodist preachers were sharing the gospel in America.

But with freedom and the ability to show himself publicly, back in 1778, also came news from England that Emily had been married. Francis read the letter from his mother with difficulty. Tears blurred his vision and a deep pain stabbed at his heart. He was, at the same time, devastated and relieved. He would never marry the girl he loved; and yet she had married a man who, by all accounts according to Francis' mother, was a strong man of faith and adored Emily. Francis need not worry about Emily's welfare any more. That was in the hands of a man who could certainly care for her better than he himself could ever hope—and in the hands of God Himself.

Francis wept that night. He walked to the shore of the Nanticoke River near Chesapeake Bay, found a stump on which to sit and pondered his life as light from a full moon played games upon the waters flowing past him—waters flowing by—on their way, somewhere. He felt like that water. Carried along by gravity with no say in the matter. Sadness tightened its grip on him. What was his future? He was alone, without family, somewhere in the wilderness that was called America. Even the future of where he lived was very much in question. Doubts crept into his mind, like little spiders slithering through a crevice between floorboards. Then fears about his own godliness slithered their way in, like cockroaches drawn to darkness, those uncertainties that he often dealt with in his regular battles against depression and against feelings of unworthiness.

Then the scripture blew into his mind like a windstorm, alerting him to God's presence. "For we are God's workmanship, created in Christ Jesus to do good works, which God prepared in advance for us to do."

God's "workmanship"—one of the meanings of the Greek "*poema*" being "great epic poem"—which God prepared—in advance—for us to do. God Himself, from His throne room, had prepared Francis' life and, hallelujah!, God knew what He was doing!

An odd combination of warmth in his chest and a chilly tingle down his spine spoke a silent "amen" to Francis' thoughts. He looked beyond the water, into the darkness, and said aloud, "Emily, I love you. But God loves you even more. He had the better choice for you." He hesitated, his voice cracking, and added, "And I believe He has the better choice for me as well."

Francis looked back on that revelation that night as the Lord's deliverance and as marching orders for one of His soldiers. The apostle Paul had written that if a preacher of the Word must marry, he must, rather than burn with lust; but if he can bear to live alone, he should, for that is the better thing. A hard thing for Francis; a sad thing to accept; but now, with Emily married, an easier struggle with which to deal.

•••••

Although dangers waited around every turn in the path ahead, the ability to travel had been the end of agony for Francis. He felt free—free, indeed—from the constricting stranglehold of confinement. And it felt so right—so right—that to rest for one day seemed like imprisonment. With the governor's "letter of freedom," as he called it, in one hand, Francis was able to travel through colonial troops. With his Bible in his other hand, and a continual prayer lifted to God's ears, he was able to avoid the British and Loyalist armies.

He now determined that he would not hide from anyone on either side of the conflict. One sunny day in June, riding with his waistcoat off and enjoying the warmth of the sun, his head was buried in Wesley's *Notes upon the New Testament*.

Pop-Pop-Pop! Shots were fired up ahead of him, but he paid them slight attention. Wesley was expounding on Matthew chapter eight, verse twenty, where Jesus says: "Foxes have holes and birds of the air have nests, but the Son of Man has no place to lay his head." To this, Wesley wrote that Jesus was, in effect, telling His followers: "Therefore, don't follow me from any view of temporal advantage."

Pop-Pop-Pop! Volleys persisted, closer now. Francis closed his eyes. He numbered his "temporal advantages." He had a horse, saddle and saddlebag; a water pot and frying pan; his Bible, Hebrew and Greek lexicons and a couple commentaries; a British quid and less than an American dollar; a wedge of bacon cooked the previous night; a quill pen, ink and paper, and, well, nothing else. He had given away his only spare shirt, pants and vest to a young itinerant preacher in sore need a few days before.

Pop-Pop-Pop! Muskets fired iron balls over his head now. Eyes still closed, with knees urging Silver Fox slowly onward, Francis prayed, *Lord, You know my heart. What 'temporal advantage' I ever had, I left in England. No house, no roof over my head, and no pillow to rest that head on. No family, not enough possessions for a thief to bother himself with. The only 'advantage' I want is Your presence in my life! Your fire shot up in my bones! Oh, Lord, I am flesh and bones and sometimes I do want—a hot meal, a cool drink. Forgive my carelessness, Father!*

Pop-Pop-Pop! The bullets seemed to be behind him now, but Francis wasn't sure; his eyes were still shut tight, a tear meandering down the nose of his bowed head. On he rode, praying for the protection and salvation of those men and boys who were firing deadly lead at one another. Did they know the preciousness of life? Did they think on whether they would survive this day, this hour, this very minute?

Francis rode on. He had to get to the next town before sunset, for he hoped to preach that night. An hour later, he reached his destination. Dismounting Silver Fox, he pulled open the flap of his saddlebag in order to store his Wesley book and noticed a hole in the leather. A bullet hole? He pulled the saddlebag from the horse and set it down on the sidewalk beside him, then proceeded to empty the contents. When the bag was empty he peered inside and there, at the bottom, he found a musket ball.

He remembered a statement by a Christian soldier he had met. When asked if he feared the bullet with his name written on it, the soldier replied, "No. I fear all those bullets that say, 'Anonymous'!"

While he was riding between the two battling armies, one of the bullets had pierced his saddlebag, missing him by inches.

That night Francis preached on two scriptures: "Now is the day of salvation" and "The hour has come for you to wake up from your slumber."

Holding up the bullet between his thumb and forefinger so that his audience could see, Francis asked, "You who have not bowed your knees to Jesus, are you so very sure a bullet engraved with your name or 'Anonymous' will not find you tonight? Satan and his minions are rubbing their hands in glee at the thought that, at any moment, with a bullet lodged in a deadly place, you could instantly be transmitted to the flames of hell."

•••••

Despite the dangers, Francis hoped to travel as long as he

lived. He realized that traveling and preaching were his health, life and all, for soul and body. Within the first six months of release from the confines of Judge White's home, he had traveled twenty-six hundred miles.

Every major town in the colonies had a newspaper, and Francis grabbed one whenever he could. From Massachusetts to Georgia, the war had rambled on. It was David versus Goliath—the mostly untrained, outnumbered colonists against the world's mightiest armed forces.

At sea, John Paul Jones had gained fame for his ship's victory against a British frigate at sea. The French had signed a treaty with America in 1778 and agreed to provide military supplies. In 1779 Spain had joined France as an ally at about the same time that Great Britain declared war on the Dutch for trading with the French and Americans.

More than one near-mutiny among colonial forces had to be squelched, including one in March 1783 when General George Washington talked his officers out of a rebellion against the authority of Congress, in effect preserving the young republic. American and British forces dealt bloody defeats to one another in Rhode Island, the Carolinas, Georgia, Virginia, New York, and elsewhere until, on August 30, 1781, Count de Grasse's French fleet arrived off Yorktown, Virginia, and de Grasse's troops joined Lafayette's forces to cut off Cornwallis' army from any retreat by land. The French were in the war for real now, their naval fleet dealing British battle ships a major defeat at Chesapeake Bay. In October 1781, British troops at Yorktown surrendered to General Washington and within months Loyalists began leaving America, heading north to Nova Scotia and New Brunswick.

Finally, on April 11, 1783, five months after the final battle, the American Congress officially declared an end to the Revolutionary War.

Two weeks later, Francis rode Silver Fox into Philadelphia for the first time in a year. The British had not yet withdrawn occupation of Philadelphia even though they had lost the war. Emotions ran the gamut from distress, bitterness, hate and unforgiveness, to joy and high expectations.

The city was all in motion. Stores were full of goods. Great trade was going on. It was a strange, almost eerie time.

All things prosper except religion and righteousness, Francis thought, as he walked from the livery the two blocks to Richard Boardman's former home, which was being used as a resting place for itinerant Methodist preachers passing through the city. The house was empty as Francis entered it.

"Hello!" he called, his voice echoing down the hallway and up the staircase. No response. He began to remove his waistcoat when he noticed, directly in front of him on a side table, an envelope with his name printed in large letters upon it.

Opening it, he pulled out a letter. It was from Philip Marchinton, telling Francis that Marchinton and others from the Methodist Society in Philadelphia were boarding a ship to leave the country. Scheduled to catch the tide, it was leaving at three-thirty in the afternoon. That afternoon! Francis pulled his watch from his watch pocket. Three o'clock!

Not wasting a moment, he pulled his coat back on and hurried out the door to find Marchinton.

As he hustled down the street, he thought of the fate of Marchinton and others among his friends who were Loyalists to the crown. As Loyalists, they were caught on the wrong end of the American victory. In 1775 Congress had passed a resolution calling for the arrest of all Loyalists who were dangerous to "the liberties of America."

Nevertheless, few were jailed, even though the Germans in Pennsylvania stayed out of the Revolution as did many Quakers and most of the Highland Scots who had immigrated to the Carolinas. And even Samuel Seabury, an Anglican clergyman, remained free although he had declared, "If I must be enslaved let it be by a king at least, and not by a parcel of upstart lawless committeemen. If I must be devoured, let me be devoured by the jaws of a lion, and not gnawed to death by rats and vermin."

In 1779, acting on the authority given it by the General Assembly, the Supreme Executive Council confiscated the holdings of all Loyalists. Marchinton's four hundred acres and buildings in West Bradford were among those taken.

Loyalists had suffered abuse upon abuse—even threats of tar-and-feathering like that done to the Boston Commissioner of Customs John Malcolm a month after the Boston Tea Party—for remaining loyal to King George the Third. Today was the final blow: expulsion from their homeland.

The week before he arrived, Francis had heard that thousands of Loyalists were setting sail this day, April 26, from New York and Philadelphia, fleeing America for Canada. That would bring the total to about one hundred thousand who had fled the colonics.

Turning a street corner and heading toward the sea, Francis knew it was God-ordained that he arrive when he did. He needed to be at the wharf to minister to these people and pray them Godspeed. After they set sail, he doubted he would see them again this side of heaven.

Hurrying now, Francis furiously scanned the faces in the crowd. He saw several he knew, but his prizes would be Philip Marchinton, John Mann and Charles White, who were leaders of the Methodist Society there.

The men and women in the crowd were from all places in society: bakers, carpenters, millers, coopers, tanners, attorneys, butchers, breeches makers, farmers, laborers and clerks of the market.

Women, their bonnets tied tightly about their chins, anxiously kept their children close about them like mother hens encircling their chicks under their wings. Men, faces taut with tension and concern, grabbed the handles of heavy trunks and, with their sons on the other end, lugged them toward the wharf. Those trunks, Francis knew, contained all the worldly belongings the families could stuff into them.

Ships' crewmen hollered to one another, giving and taking orders. It was a sort of ordered pandemonium, if there were such a thing.

Then he saw Marchinton. A trader by occupation now called a traitor by his own countrymen. He seemed calm in the midst of the turmoil, standing nearly a head taller than any other in the crowd, as Francis made his way through the throng toward him.

"Philip," Francis called. "Philip!"

Philip miraculously heard his name called through the din and searched out its source. Upon spotting Francis, his eyes went wide.

"Bishop!"

The two friends maneuvered past people and grasped each others' hands. Then Philip drew Francis to him and hugged him tightly.

"Frank, I thought I'd never lay eyes on you again. I'm so glad you're here."

"I just arrived in town moments ago and saw your letter in the foyer of the Boardman home. I hurried as quickly as I could." Francis looked about. "Are John Mann and Charles White here?"

"Yes, I was just with them five minutes ago."

"I'd like to pray with you and your families before you board ship."

Philip glanced down at his watch. "We're boarding in just a few minutes."

"Then let's hurry!" Francis said, and the two men went to search for their friends.

As they searched for the other Society members, Philip told Francis they were sailing for the northern shore of Nova Scotia, to Pictou County. Others had gone on before them and started a society there. Philip tried to be uplifting, to put on a smile, but Francis could read pain behind the mask. So much had been ripped from this man for the choice he had made to support the king. His roots had gone deep here, his business had flourished, and he and his wife had been leaders in the community. Now? Well, now was another life—obviously one of personal upheaval for him, Sarah, and their three beautiful teenage daughters. Perhaps a future elsewhere was best.

It took ten minutes to gather everyone, and the first mate was calling, "All aboard!" but a group of about twenty congregated around Francis. Encircled by families he loved, most of whom he had actually led to the Lord, Francis tried to fight off tears. It was a losing fight and he stammered through a prayer: "Dear Lord God Almighty, You watch over Your children with a mighty right arm. I present these brothers and sisters to you to care and provide shelter for, to guide and direct. I ask that you empower them with the Holy Spirit to accomplish the mission You have for each of them; to move forward in an anointing that will draw the unsaved to Your throne room for salvation. I pray You would imbue them with a desire to sit in your lap daily, feed on your Word, drink your living water and continue to grow into wonderful disciples of Christ. Be their Rock, their Protector, their High Tower. And have your angels watch over them in all their ways and hold them in the palm of their hands so they do not strike their feet against a stone.

"I leave them in your marvelous hands, Father! Bless them and keep them and overflow them with Your shalom—body, soul and spirit." Francis looked about him, at the bowed heads, unabashed and unashamed of their faith as they stood in the midst of hundreds of people bustling by them en route to the ship. He took a deep breath and almost whispered, "Amen."

Minutes later, Francis stood at the wharf and waved as the ship sailed away. A thought grabbed him. Was he standing in the same spot that he occupied when Richard Wright sailed for England after John Wesley called them home? He looked down at his feet, at the railing before him and at the harbor. Yes, he thought. Yes, he was. Others always seemed to be leaving while he stayed behind. He had to keep focused and pray. *One more soul, Lord! One more!*

Then he heard that still small voice. *I am sending them to spread the gospel. It came from England to America. Now it is going from America to Nova Scotia. I do have a plan, Francis.*

He smiled at the admonition. He looked heavenward. "Of course You do, Lord."

CHAPTER 6

Gallows Evangelism

November 1784 arrived cold and bitter in Kent County, Delaware. Leaves had left the trees and hibernation had set in for all sorts of nature. On Sunday, the 14th, Francis rode Silver Fox hard, trying to get to his destination on time. Today was the day! He had not yet met Thomas Coke, but had received word that Coke had arrived from England and was to address the congregation at Barratt's Chapel at ten o'clock this morning.

John Wesley had written Francis a letter spelling out the plans. Wesley's good friend, Coke, was instructed to find Francis and the two were to discuss the future of American Methodism.

Francis had preached at Barratt's Chapel himself. It was built just four years earlier on land donated by Philip Barratt, a prominent political figure in Kent County who also funded the construction.

Francis looked to his left at the sun and guessed it was time for the meeting to begin. He was close by, in the midst of the forest where the chapel stood. He urged his horse on, not wanting to miss a moment of the morning's service.

A few minutes later, the two-story brick structure came into view through the trees. Horses, buggies and wagons filled a pasture surrounding the chapel. Francis found a hitching post for Silver Fox, grabbed his Bible and hurried to the entrance, where he was met by Marlon Gray. "Mister Asbury!" Marlon said, sticking out his hand in welcome. "Mister Coke is preaching and we have a seat right up front for you, next to the Widow Barratt."

"Widow?"

Marlon was startled. "You haven't heard?"

"No, Marlon. What happened?"

"Philip died of pneumonia, sir. Only a week ago."

Francis' heart fell like an anvil to the ground. Philip—dead. A champion for God, a man who not only labored for the Lord but showed his devotion through brick and mortar. Francis shook his head. "How is Harriet doing, Marlon?"

"You know Sister Barratt. I think she's putting on a good face for the rest of us, sir."

Yes, that would be Harriet. Strong. Resolute. She had probably told their two grown sons that she would remain in her own home, care for herself, and wouldn't be a worry for anyone.

Francis nodded toward the church. "The service has started?"

"Mister Coke is preaching."

"Then I'll sit in the back."

"No place to sit, sir. There must be six hundred here today. Standing room only. About a dozen preachers are seated up front with Sister Barratt. As I said, sir, a seat beside Sister Barratt is reserved for you. Please join 'em."

Francis disliked people milling about during his sermons and didn't want to do so to Coke, but acquiesced and walked quietly and quickly to his seat.

Harriet Barratt's face brightened at the sight of him and tears began to brim up at the corners of her eyes. She squeezed his arm. Francis passed her his handkerchief and planted a brotherly kiss on her forehead.

"And the Lord will lift us up!" Coke's booming voice grabbed Francis' attention. He looked up to the pulpit. Before the congregation stood a short man, but with a voice of authority.

Coke looked directly at Harriet and said, "David wrote in Psalm one hundred sixteen, verse fifteen that 'precious in the sight of the Lord is the death of His saints.' Dear lady, our Lord has been preparing a place for us in heaven since His resurrection seventeen hundred and fifty-two years ago. Know that your beloved is in

God's presence, awash in His holiness, at home and at peace."

Coke looked quickly at Francis—and Francis knew he was guessing who he was—then scanned the congregation. "Who knows of God's timing, or can argue with it? We can't remember what happened a week ago and can not predict what will happen tomorrow. But, acknowledging this, we must trust that God—for whom there is no beginning and no end—knows precisely the vagaries and battles that rise and fall over days and years and centuries. What He allows, we should accept—with as pleasing an attitude as possible. Is it difficult? Yes.

"Paul tells us to 'think on things that are lovely, pure and of good report.' Is it difficult? Yes.

"But consider this: our time on earth is but a butterfly's flitter in the midst of eternity. Do you think it punishment when God allows us to pass from this life? Do you for one minute think life here on earth superior to that in glory?

"Our bodies—and our brother Barratt's body—may return to the dust from which it was formed, but his spirit—his spirit? It has already risen to the heavens and he worships where we all wish to be: at the throne of the risen Christ!"

Harriet gasped next to Francis and he felt her shake. He knew that she could barely contain herself from rising up and singing, "Hallelujah!"

Before them, Coke continued on, his voice strong with conviction. "Absent from the body is present with the Lord!

"Death has been swallowed up in victory. Where, O death, is your victory? Where, O death, is your sting?!"

The hall rang out. "Praise His Name!" "Hallelujah!" "Bless the Lamb!" "Glory!"

"'Glory' is right," Coke said. "Brother Barratt is rejoicing in glory!"

All over the church men stood and began applauding even as they called out, "Thank You, Jesus! Holy Man, Holy God!" "Prepare the way, Lord!" "Hallelujah to the Lamb!"

Coke went on to administer the sacraments of baptism and communion—the first time in America by ordained Methodist clergy. Afterwards, when Coke descended from the pulpit, Asbury stood and grasped him, planting a brotherly kiss on his cheek.

"Brother Asbury?" Coke asked.

"Frank, sir."

"Thomas, then," Coke said. The joy of the two men at that moment, the feeling of a shared faith, a common calling, a drive to go to the ends of the earth to share the gospel of Christ—all these knit the two men together. Francis could see the love of Christ in his new friend's eyes.

"If it were not for you, Frank," Coke said, "I would not be here. We Methodists would not be welcomed. We would be seen as Loyalists, sympathizers with the crown."

Francis nodded agreement, but refused self-congratulations.

"Sister Barratt is hosting us at her home. Our brethren here," Coke motioned to several young men around them, "will join us and we can begin to chart the path for the church here in America."

That is exactly what happened. That evening the entire group, joined by Richard Whatcoat, formulated plans to bring all the preachers together at Lovely Lane Meetinghouse in Baltimore on Christmas Day to form the Methodist Episcopal Church.

Francis and Coke spoke privately concerning the future management of their affairs in America, appointing superintendents, elders and deacons. Coke planned to travel back to England sporadically to maintain communications with the leaders in England in the years ahead.

Coke had been ousted from his church for preaching Methodist doctrine. As a full presbyter in the Church of England, he was already authorized to administer the sacraments. John Wesley had consecrated him and sent him to America to consecrate Francis.

Six weeks later in a three-day conference which began on Friday, December 24, 1784, Francis and Coke were unanimously elected to the superintendency of the church. Coke then ordained Francis. The group divided the new country into districts and determined to assign a preacher to each district.

Sam Brackett broke in. "Do you mean you preached all those

years here in America before being ordained?"

Francis nodded.

"But why?"

"We had no one here with the power to ordain. Should we have gone to Presbyterians to be ordained Episcopal Methodists? Or to Episcopalians, who at that time had no bishop or power of ordination in America until they applied to the British Parliament? It was not until seventeen-eighty-five that this body passed a law for the express purpose authorizing their bishops to consecrate and ordain bishops for the thirteen States of America."

"Obviously not," Sam said.

"Or could we subscribe to Calvinist articles? Surely not. Or could we submit to locality? By no means. Let local men ordain local men, baptize, or re-baptize local men. We knew we must shape our course and prepare to meet the different annual conferences from Maine to Georgia and to the Mississippi, and try sacredly to maintain our traveling plan and support a true missionary, apostolic church.

"Remember, the Methodist church was the first organized after the establishment of peace in seventeen eighty-three, and the Protestant Episcopalians were not organized as a church until after there was a law passed by the British Parliament.

"We made a lot of progress during that Christmas Conference. What a time! Celebrating our Lord's birth and charting the birth of the church in America." Francis shook his head in wonder. "We not only divided the country into districts and assigned preachers to those districts, we prescribed duties and set parameters for their work. No man could locate without order or he would forfeit his official standing. No preacher was to be stationary more than two years; no presiding elder more than four years. If they remained beyond that time, the constitution would remove them; and all were to be movable at the pleasure of the superintendent whenever he found it necessary for the good of the cause of Christ. Every traveling minister was required to say to his parishioners: 'I am not obliged to serve you another year; I will speak to the superintendent, who will not impose me on you a second year.'"

Abigail interrupted, "Francis, we love Pastor Matthews, but we did not want his predecessor, Boynton Lasley, to leave. I never understood why we couldn't keep him longer."

"You're not alone, my dear," Francis said. "But the fact is that this is in keeping with the first-century church. All the ancient, imperial, Latin, and Greek churches were apostolic—carrying the gospel to the ends of the known earth—and episcopalian—ruled by bishops.

"I'm bold to say, my dear, that the apostolic order of things was lost in the first century, when church governments were adulterated and filled with corruption. At the Reformation, the reformers beat off only a part of the rubbish, which put a stop to the rapid increase of absurdities at that time; but how they have increased since!

"Recollect the state of the government and discipline of the different churches when the Lord raised up that great and good man, John Wesley, who formed an evangelical society in England. What we have done is carry on the tradition of Saint Paul, Barnabas, Silas, Mark, Timothy, Titus, Tychicus, Archippus, Trophimus, Artemas, Luke, Epaphroditus and other holy apostolic men who set an example for us through the ages.

"They carried the Word throughout the known world. It may be a crooked and muddy succession since their day, but our church records and Conference journals will show that we have followed their lead, traveling vast tracks of country to share the gospel. I myself have visited nine Conferences annually for nearly three decades."

Francis looked softly at Abigail. "I'm sorry you lost Boynton. I know he was a blessing to you, but today he is a blessing to others, elsewhere. And you have Robert now, to bring the Word to you in his own way. This way of keeping moving allows neither one of them to get stuck, if you will, in a rut."

Abigail shrugged in acceptance and offered a brief smile.

Francis turned to Nicholas. "We were in great haste and did much business in a little time at that Conference. It was challenging, but exciting and invigorating. It was a new work. A great undertaking!"

Nicholas nodded, "The latest Conference report says that in forty-five years our poor little 'daughter mission church' in America has overgrown her mother in Europe of near seventy years standing.

"And," Francis said, "we've done so with no doctors of law and divinity—no great speakers or writers, none famous among us of whom we can boast. All has been done simply with the power of the Holy Ghost."

Sam spoke up, "It all paid off for me personally, Francis. As Bishop Coke said, without your conviction to stay here in the colonies, the Methodist Episcopal Church would most likely have not survived here. And, taken a step further, if that were the case, I most likely would still be a sinner buried in the filth of my sins."

•••••

Francis beamed to hear Sam mention his salvation. It thrilled his heart to hear it.

"I'm sorry to have interrupted you, Francis," Sam said. "Please tell us what happened then."

Francis flashed back to the period following that famous Christmas Conference.

In 1785 Francis was confronted with the stiffest test to his resolve not to wed. While visiting with Patrick Henry, who had recently been elected governor of Virginia for the fourth time, he had received word that his good friend Colonel Henry Willis had died from pneumonia at his home in Fredericksburg. Francis was aghast. He had just seen Henry two months before and he was a healthy specimen of a man. While Mildred had lost her first husband, Roger Gregory, to illness, Henry had suffered the loss of his wife Elizabeth as well, and this union—this new love found between them—had been a godsend for both. But now. Now, what would Mildred do? She had to care for her own three daughters and the two sons and a daughter from Henry's first marriage. Henry had owned a lot of land and their home was sufficient, but could

Mildred care for this many children alone? Could she possibly find a man willing to marry a woman with six children in tow?

Francis had immediately ridden to the Willis homestead. It was a four-day trip with little rest except to feed Silver Fox and himself. They traveled through Hewlet and Cedar Fork and Ladysmith and Cedon—all places he would normally preach two or three times a day before leaving. When he and Silver Fox finally arrived at the Willis home, they were both exhausted. Mildred met him at the door and offered up a weak smile of gratitude for his coming. Following her out the door came four girls between the ages of four and twelve and two sons ten and sixteen years old. A frequent guest of theirs, Francis knew them well. Good children, now all orphans!

As he stood beside Mildred they all gathered up to him and he encircled the six children in his arms, kissing the head of each one. A surge of love overflowed and for a minute the feeling of fatherhood enveloped him like a cloak—a comfortable cloak at that. Oh, how he wished that they were his!

The next three days, Francis stayed overnight with a neighbor, to keep an assurance of propriety, but spent the days ministering to Mildred and the children. He told tales of heaven and its glory, its streets of gold and gates of pearl. He told them that their father, his dear friend, was sitting at the feet of the Lord and singing praises to His glorious name. All the while, he struggled with who would care for this lovely family. Could he, should he? He loved Mildred as a sister in Christ. He loved the children as his own. Why not, Lord?

He need not even have asked God the question, for he knew the answer even as the query left his lips. And yet he asked it again and again, hoping for a different response, but at the same time concerned he would be granted that wish. In the end, the Lord assured Francis that He loved Mildred and the children more than Francis ever could; that He would provide her a husband or be her groom Himself; and that He would provide all her needs according to His riches in glory, which far exceeded the pittance, about thirty pounds a year, Francis earned. Francis could continue to love and support them in other ways but was, himself, to be husband to no person.

Needing to leave for the state capital, where he was to preach to the Virginia Legislature, Francis gathered the family on the fourth morning.

With Mildred's approval, he began. "I loved your father as a brother and you as my own children," he said, looking each of them in the eye. Tears began to creep into the eyes of Josephine and Amanda, the eight- and ten-year-old girls. "I wish I could stay to watch over you, but there is One who is a far better Father than I could ever be to you and He has promised me He will do just that.

"I was in prayer last night and the Lord reminded me that Jesus, in Mark chapter ten, took up the children in His arms, put His hands on them and blessed them. Just as Isaac blessed Jacob and Esau and as Jacob blessed Joshua, and just as God told the priests to pray the blessings on the Jewish people in Numbers chapter six, so, as a pastor would bless his flock and as a father would bless his children, I would like to bless you this morning."

"Oh, yes, Bishop!" little four-year-old Natalie piped up. She probably didn't even understand what Francis was saying, but the other children agreed in concert.

Each in turn, from the oldest boy, Jonathan, to the youngest of all, Natalie, Francis laid his hands upon their heads and prayed a blessing that gripped each one's heart—for the Lord showed him the gifts and calling He had on each child's life. Francis recalled Romans chapter eleven, verse twenty-nine: "The gifts and calling of God are irrevocable."

Laying his right hand on Jonathan's head and his left hand on his shoulder, Francis prayed: "Lord God Almighty, giver of all good things, bless this young man with the true faithfulness that his namesake, King David's best friend, possessed; with the wisdom of Solomon, the faith of Abraham, the zeal of Peter. Bless Jonathan your son, Father, with an overflowing of all the talents and abilities we can already see in him. He has the compassionate, loving heart of a man of God and the creativity of an artist. Lavish him with the ability to use those gifts to further your kingdom; help him to be a light in the darkness, a joy among sadness, an encourager to his brothers and sisters and a helpful hand to his mother.

"Jonathan, may you always worship the Lord your God. May you discern wisely, judge righteously, and act faithfully. May you be blessed with a virtuous spouse. May your children be as olive trees in the House of God and may you have health, wealth and success."

After Francis had blessed all the children, he called Mildred to him and had the entire family stand in a circle, holding hands.

Quoting from Numbers chapter six, he declared, "The Lord bless you and keep you; the Lord make His face shine upon you, and be gracious to you; the Lord lift up His countenance upon you, and give you peace."

He nodded to Mildred, who took the cue to bring a bowl filled with honeycomb. She took a spoon and called the children to her. "Oftentimes, when Jewish parents bless their children they place a dollop of honey on their tongue," she said. "The taste of honey is to remind you that God's Word is sweet, something to desire, to savor. It's something to treasure. And it's something to seek after."

She put a spoonful of honey into the mouth of each of her children.

Shortly afterward, grabbing his coat, Francis said his good-byes, promising to visit them as often as possible. He hugged Mildred and the children, mounted Silver Fox and smiled down on them.

Natalie cried, "Can I have one last hug, Bishop? Just one?"

Francis nodded to Jonathan, who passed the child up to him and Francis held her close to him.

"I love you, child," he said, running his fingers along her dimpled cheek.

"I love you, too, Bishop. And Jesus does, too."

"Does He?" Francis smiled.

"Yes, I know, because He is in me."

"He is?" Even knowing the child as he did, Francis was taken aback that a four-year-old would say this.

"Yes, He's in my heart and on my lips," Natalie said, and she pointed to her head and added, "And He's in my head!"

"Oh, that's a *good* thing," Francis said. "I'll always remember that, dear one."

Squeezing her to him one last time and kissing her forehead, he handed the girl back to Jonathan, tipped his hat to Mildred, and rode off southward, turning his face away quickly so that they could not see the tears that were making their way down his cheek.

•••••

Little Thomas sat quietly, riveted as he listened, turning Francis' hat around in his hands. As he did, he came to the bullet hole. Poking his index finger through the hole, his eyes lit up with a question and he looked up at Francis. "Didja ever get shot closer 'n this, or that bullet in your saddlebag?"

"Ha!" Francis exclaimed. "I'll tell you a 'closer-than' story, son."

Francis recalled a day, in the foothills of Tennessee in 1779. Rain pelted down in torrents—large, pregnant drops that splattered on his hat and rainjacket. With two snaps of his tongue, he urged on Silver Fox.

He softly sang two verses of one of his favorite hymns by William Cowper:

> *The dearest idol I have known,*
> *Whate'er that idol be,*
> *Help me to tear it from Thy throne*
> *And worship only Thee.*
>
> *So shall my walk be close with God,*
> *Calm and serene my frame,*
> *So purer the light shall mark the road*
> *That leads me to the Lamb.*

And he prayed he would be able to reach their destination before dark, but knew this would be another of the thousands of nights he had spent in the out-of-doors cuddled up to his horse. It certainly looked like the rain would continue. He thought of the latest adage going around the States about horrible weather: "Nobody out but the crows and the Methodists."

He laughed at the thought and patted Silver Fox below her ear.

He looked up, squinting into the gray overcast, darkening by the moment. The trail wasn't only getting difficult to follow but treacherous as well. A raindrop the size of a quarter splattered in his left eye. He winced, pulled his longcoat tighter about him and hunched down over the horse's neck. "Up ahead here, girl. Just up ahead."

After another fifty yards or so of slopping through deepening mud, he heard through the din of the rainfall what he thought to be a bird call. Bird call? In this rain? He pulled Silver Fox to a halt and listened. Another bird call, but this was no bird! Leaning down to his horse's ear, he urged her on. "Giddyup, Silver Fox!"

Silver Fox responded without hesitation, as if she were a child just waiting for her parent to give her the go-ahead to run through the rain and mud, kicking up a storm in her wake. Slop, sloppy and sloppier—those were the conditions.

Francis turned to look behind him through the ferocious downpour. Could these be the Indians who burned down the village twelve miles to the east? The bird calls would suggest that. Murdering men, women and children was an occupation for these savages, hired by the British but with a grudge of their own as well. One itinerant preacher would be a mere afterthought in comparison to the dozens they had massacred.

Francis gauged the distance to the nearest village compared to the closeness of his pursuers. *This does not bode well for the child of Joseph and Elizabeth Asbury*, he thought wryly.

Another bird call. Closer this time—probably within sight. *If they can see me, they can catch me*, Francis reasoned. And he thought of the irony: he did not stand to be killed by his own countrymen, nor by a colonist; if it happened now, it would be at the hands of some Indian who—poor soul—most likely had never heard the gospel.

He said aloud, to his God nearby: "We need some help here, Lord! A miracle! Cover us! Clothe us with yourself!"

Through the sounds of the drenching rain, he heard branches snap to his left and rear, and not far at that, as one of the pursuers crashed through a thicket of small alders. A swishing sound went by his head and, in the same instant he felt a sharp sting above his right ear and he caught sight of an arrow as it pierced a tree before him and to his right with a *poing*.

Suddenly, unexpectedly, like stepping from a lighted room into a dark night, Francis and Silver Fox were cloaked in a fog bank. What little light had filtered through the dense forest was instantly shut out. Francis didn't know whether to pull Silver Fox to a halt, or let her go. He could barely see her mane beneath his grip on the reins. She made the decision for him. On many dark nights, Francis had let go the reins and trusted Silver Fox to follow the trail,which he could not see but she could, and get them to the next village. Today he could not see through the thick fog but, somehow, she sensed the way, slowing to a trot but continuing on.

Being gray, Silver Fox disappeared like a ghost from the sight of the pursuing Indians. Moments later, as if hitting a wall, the group of four, faces painted in war colors, were forced to turn aside. The leader shared a steely look with the others, then stared at the fog into which Francis had disappeared and screamed a trill. Francis heard the warrior scream and a chill raced down his neck. With a shrug of their shoulders, the Indians turned their horses away from the wall of darkness and headed back from where they came, mud kicking up from the hoofs of their horses.

Remembering his close call, Francis looked down at Thomas, whose eyes were wide and mouth agape. "Wow!" escaped from the boy's mouth.

"Do you know the story of Moses leading the Jewish people out of Egypt, young man?" Francis asked.

"Why, yes, sir."

"Do you know what happened when they reached the Red Sea?"

Proud that he knew the answer, Thomas crossed his arms and smiled, saying, "God stopped the sea so they could pass over."

"Very good. Do you know how God held back the Egyptians until the Jews could cross over?"

Thomas rubbed his chin and thought a few seconds, finally deciding, "No."

"Well, He did something similar to what He did for me that day," Francis said. "The angel of God had been traveling in front of the Hebrew people as they escaped Egypt. But, just then, he withdrew and went behind them, putting the pillar of cloud between them and the armies of Egypt. There was darkness on the Egyptian side of the cloud and light on the Hebrews' side."

Thomas' eyes widened. "Did you have light on your side of the cloud, Bishop?"

Francis laughed. "No, I didn't, but it sure did stop those Indians in their tracks!"

Abigail said, "You certainly have had some close calls with death, Bishop."

"Well, I have to admit that getting wounded that day and shot at a couple of days ago coming here were the closest." Francis chuckled. "Funny thing, both times have been shots at my head. Maybe God is trying to tell me something—like, 'Don't let yourself get a swelled head, Francis. *I* know how little you know'."

Everyone laughed.

"Actually, I do believe it happened for a purpose, and that's as good a purpose as any. The Lord is omniscient, you know. Nothing happens except that He allows. And, I always have a reminder of that day."

"What's that, Francis?" asked Nicholas.

Francis said to Thomas, "Let me see your hand, son."

Thomas extended his arm. Francis took his hand and moved it to a place just above his right ear. "Can you feel the bump there?"

Thomas nodded his head.

"Whenever I happen to touch that bump, I remember not to think too highly of myself. And I remember God's deliverance that day. From where did that fog appear?"

It was a rhetorical question, but Thomas piped up, "Why, from that big angel, sir!"

"Right you are, son," said Sam, rising from his chair by the fireplace. "And that's a good time to get you off to bed, so you end the day on a high note." He scooped Thomas out of Francis' lap and wheeled him into the air. Thomas giggled shrilly. When Sam set him down on the floor, the boy said, "Again, Daddy. Again!"

Sam lifted him again, dangled him upside down and walked off toward the child's bedroom.

"Interesting how children have no fear when they're in their father's hands, isn't it?" offered Nicholas.

"And it's what God wants from us," Abigail said.

"Yes, and it's a lesson I still haven't learned to its fullest," Francis said. "James tells us that lack of faith is sin, and I too often find that that's where I am."

"Not you, sir!" Nicholas objected.

"Yes, me. I look back through the years where I've written in my journal and what I read more often than not, Nicholas, indicates that I'm but a few rungs up that ladder."

"Then none of us have hope, Francis," Abigail said.

"With God anything is possible," Francis smiled. "And, in you, I see a Proverbs thirty-one woman."

"Well, that's very kind of you," Abigail said. Stifling a yawn, she added, "This Proverbs thirty-one woman needs to be off to bed and get some sleep so she can start a new day early, cook breakfast, wash some clothes, darn some socks and make sure her family is 'dressed in scarlet.'"

Catching Abigail's allusion to Proverb's thirty-one's "dressed-in-scarlet" scripture, Francis said, "Ah, you know the proverb."

"She knows them all," interjected Sam, who had just come back down the stairs, "especially the one about ants keeping busy."

Abigail laughed lightly. "If we don't keep busy in this wilderness, we'll perish."

"All hard work brings a profit, but mere talk leads only to poverty," Nicholas quoted.

"Commit to the Lord whatever you do, and your plans will succeed," Francis added. "That's been one of my guiding scriptures."

"It appears to have worked, Francis," Sam said. "It wasn't long after the Revolution that you were promoted to lead the church here in America, was it?"

"After the war, John Wesley ordained Thomas Coke as his American superintendent. Tom, in turn, ordained me at the Baltimore Christmas Conference in 1784. That gave birth to the Methodist Episcopal Church. On Christmas Day, they ordained me a deacon, and the day after an elder, and the next day as superintendent. It was a whirlwind. As Tom said, 'We were in great haste and did much business in a little time.'"

"Wasn't it soon after that that Mister Coke returned to England?" Nicholas asked.

"Yes." Francis shook his head. "It was then that Mister Wesley wanted to strap the title 'general superintendent' on me, and I changed it simply to 'bishop.' My, did he get angry at that, thinking the title prideful and writing me a scathing rebuke. But, I explained to him, by letter, that I figured you can save two people in the time it takes you to spit out *that* title. And, it uses less ink!"

Sam, Abigail and Nicholas all laughed.

"Besides," Francis added, "'bishop' is biblical; I've never seen 'general superintendent' anywhere in Scripture. And, so that our members wouldn't feel 'ruled over' from abroad, I thought it best they were able to confirm appointment as leader."

Sam looked at Abigail and said, "You go off to bed, Abby. I'd like to hear some more of the Bishop's story." He looked at Francis. "Unless you'd rather get to bed yourself?"

Francis shook his head. "No, I'm sort of enjoying this—in a melancholy way."

Sam knelt before the fireplace and poked at a couple of logs to liven up the flames, then sat back down in his fireside chair.

Nicholas asked, "Can you take us back to the Revolution, Bishop? To the end of it, I mean."

"Of course."

•••••

Francis rode into Burlington, Pennsylvania, one day and there was a commotion in the streets. It appeared people were gathering for something.

"What's happening?" he asked one young man who was leaning against a fence post.

"Thief's gonna kick the clouds before the hotel door," he answered.

"What?"

"Thief's gonna be hanged," answered another fellow standing beside the young man.

Francis then looked up and noticed a Newman's lift—gallows. Indeed, a public execution was about to be held.

He wondered what would draw such crowds. Was it fascination? Entertainment? Diversion from the struggles of the day? Or simple blood lust? He supposed it was a different lure for different people. It was certainly a community ritual that condemned the crime and meted out retribution for the wrong done. It warned would-be law breakers, in no uncertain way, what awaited them if indeed they committed a crime, from theft to murder, and were caught. It allowed the entire citizenry, simply by showing up in person, to take part, figuratively, in cleansing the community of criminals. And it allowed the criminal to repent before them all—and before God Almighty.

Tethering Silver Fox, Francis made his way to the jailhouse which was actually the first jailhouse he had seen in America. Normally people were incarcerated in all sorts of buildings, in whatever space was available.

Stepping inside, he noted the constable, Seth Andrews, surrounded by men dealing with the logistics of the hanging.

One burly fellow dressed in black was obviously the hangman. Another, dressed in finery, was probably the mortician.

"Bishop!" Seth said, and stepped toward Francis with his hand extended.

"Seth," Francis acknowledged, shaking his hand. "What have we here?"

"We're hanging a horse thief," Seth checked his watch, "in a half-hour." He nodded toward the back of the room.

Francis followed his direction. In front of a small, barred jail cell, a man the size of an Allegheny foothill, draped with a full, bushy beard, glared at him and the constable. Behind the bars stood a mess of a young man. His clothes were dirty and tattered. His long hair hung in sweaty strands. His attempts at growing a beard had resulted in patches here and there around a face that looked too young to hang. Francis guessed his age at eighteen, twenty perhaps.

"Horse thief," Francis said just above a whisper.

"Caught dead to rights, Bishop," Seth said. "Name's Jacob Trimble. That's his father, John. People call him 'Mountain.'"

Francis nodded. No surprise there.

"Moved in since you were here last. Lives out in the woods. Meanest man around. If he and a bear were in a stare-down, it would be the bear that would run, whimpering, up a tree."

Francis chuckled at the imagery, but Mountain certainly carried a trunkload of hate around with him. It didn't take a spiritual person to sense that.

Francis looked at the constable. "Mind if I speak to the lad, Seth?"

"No. But I'd beware Mount Trimble. My deputy over here has a pistol ready for any shenanigans, but be leery. I mean, this fellow could probably bend those bars with one arm tied behind his back. He hasn't threatened me, mind you. Just asked to speak to his boy, and I couldn't deny him that."

Francis put his hand on the constable's arm, thanked him and stepped toward the cell.

Mountain stepped in front of Francis and challenged, "Who

are you, Mister?"

"Bishop Francis Asbury."

"Then turn around and leave."

"I'd like to speak to Jacob."

"I said leave—now." His voice was deep and threatening. There was no inkling of request in the sentence; it was a demand. He put his hands on his hips and formed a barrier to his son.

"Your son is about to die, Mister Trimble. Don't you want him to have the chance to repent before God?"

"God!" Mountain spat out the word, then spat on the ground at Francis' feet. "You can take your God and leave my sight!"

"It appears you have an argument with the Lord," Francis said, stepping closer to this huge man. He smelled the combination of sweat, whiskey and something akin to wet deerskin. "But I'm not so concerned with that at this moment as I am with Jacob. It is he, after all, who is in peril of meeting Satan face-to-face in just a few minutes."

"My boy doesn't want to hear 'bout your God, fella, so just go back to where you came from. I suppose you want a good seat at the 'show' with the rest of the bloodsuckers out there."

"I'm not here for any show, Mister Trimble, just to share the gospel with a man who is about to die. And at this point in his life, I think you can't speak for him."

"I can if I say I can."

"Really? Why don't you ask him?"

Mountain turned his head toward the young man. Jacob shuffled his hand through his unruly hair. He mumbled, "I guess so, Dad. Momma'd say I should listen."

"Your Momma's dead, boy. Died of fever. And what did her God do for her?"

The boy didn't answer.

Mountain turned to Francis with menacing eyes. "The boy's Ma, she was one of you. She almost had me hooked, too. Then sickness got her. She called out to God for healin'. Nothin'. She called out for Him to take the pain. Nothin'. Her last words were 'Take me home, Lord.' I never saw Him. He never showed up."

"And how do you know this?"

"Cause I didn't see him! Molasses and milk are more real than your God, mister."

"More tangible, perhaps, but not more real," Francis replied. He studied the man. He was angry at life, angry at the world, beyond angry with even the idea of God. "When your wife died, was she in anguish or in joy, Mister Trimble?

Mountain hesitated. But his son piped up, "She had the hugest smile on her face I ever saw!"

Francis and Mountain both turned as the boy spoke. The young man's face had entirely changed as he recalled the look on his mother's face at her death.

"She must-ve been lookin' at them pearly gates, she was so happy!" the boy went on.

Francis put his hand on Mountain's arm. "Then I'd say the Lord *did* show up, Mister Trimble—seen or unseen."

"Your opinion," Mountain said.

"And you're welcome to yours," Francis said, undaunted. "Now, may I speak to your son?"

Before Mountain could reply, the young man said, "Yes, Dad. Let him by."

Mountain stood his ground.

"Mister Trimble, do you love your son?" Francis asked.

"'Course!"

"Do you want him to have the same joy as your wife did upon her death?"

"I don't want him to die!" Mountain cried out and tears like a gusher exploded from his eyes. "He's all I got!"

Such an abandonment to feelings shocked Francis and shook him. He turned and looked at Seth, who lowered his eyes and slowly shook his head. There was no hope of mercy; the law had spoken and it was a harsh law in this land.

Francis stepped around Mountain and met no resistance. Here was this hulk of a man, who probably hadn't shown an emotion outside belligerence since his wife passed on, and he was sobbing uncontrollably in front of a room of men. Francis knew that if he could have stopped weeping he would have; but it was beyond him. What remained of his life was in this child of his, and this child was about to be hanged.

Francis stepped up to the cell bars and locked the young man's eyes with his own. "Jacob, your Mom was a Christian?"

"Yes-sir."

"Did she read the Bible to you?"

"Yes-sir. I remember a lot of the stories."

"Do you remember about Jacob, your namesake?"

Jacob thought for a moment. "No, sir, I don't suppose I do."

"Do you remember Abraham or Isaac?"

"Father Abraham!" the young man was excited that he held this tiny bit of knowledge.

"Well, Abraham's son was Isaac and his grandson was Jacob. They are the fathers of the faith, set apart by God. God selected Abraham, Isaac and Jacob to father a new race, the Jews, who would follow after Him, keep His Word and His commandments and receive all the wonderful gifts God has to share with His creation."

Jacob nodded that he understood and stole a look at his father who stood resting his head against the wall and blowing his nose.

"Jacob wrestled with a man, who was an angel of the Lord, one entire night. Finally, the angel said, 'Let me go, for it is daybreak.' But Jacob refused, saying, 'I won't let you go until you bless me.'

"'Tell me your name,' the angel said.

"'Jacob,' he replied.

"'Your name will no longer be Jacob but Israel, because you have struggled with God and with men and have overcome,' the angel said. And then the angel blessed him."

Jacob looked perplexed. "Why'd you tell me this story?"

"Israel means 'he struggles with God.'" Francis held up his index finger as if he were before a classroom. "Remember that Jacob told the Man he was wrestling with that he wouldn't let him go until he blessed him."

The young man nodded his head.

"That meant that he was acknowledging God as the source of blessing. And because he did this, the angel acknowledged Jacob as God's servant by changing his name. That was the day God gave the nation of Israel her name—and her character: people who struggle with God and with men—and who overcome. That day God allowed Jacob back into the Promised Land, where he was reunited with his brother Esau."

Jacob still looked perplexed, so Francis plowed on.

"Ever since your mother passed on, you and your father have been struggling with God, haven't you, Jacob?"

The boy nodded in agreement.

"Your father being a Mountain," Francis paused and glanced at John Trimble whose red eyes looked back at him in despair, "you decided to see eye to eye with him about his views on the Lord. Right?"

The boy nodded.

"But in your own mind, you didn't discount the existence of God, did you, Jacob? You struggled with it, but you never denied it."

The boy nodded.

Francis grabbed hold of the cell bars and fixed his eyes on Jacob. "It's an easy choice, son. But you have to make it now." He pointed outside toward the gallows. "The hangman's noose is waiting for you; we can't change that. But we can change your eternal destiny!"

Jacob began nodding exaggeratedly. "Yes, sir. Yes, sir. I want that! I do!"

Francis remained calm on the outside while his heart did flips inwardly. "In a minute, when you do, you'll be like your namesake, like Jacob-renamed-Israel. You'll have struggled with God and overcome all the obstacles that Satan has put in the way of your acceptance of your Messiah. And, Jacob, do you know what?"

"What, sir?"

"Just as Jacob was reunited in the Promised Land with his brother Esau, you'll be reunited, in heaven, with your Mom."

"Hallelujah!" The shout didn't come from Jacob, nor from Francis. When the roomful of people looked at the source of the exclamation, they saw Mountain with his arms raised almost to the ceiling, tears pouring down his cheeks and into his beard. Here was a man who had suddenly found his way out of a dungeon of despondency and misery into a lofty place of joy and peace.

Francis smiled and turned back to Jacob. "Would you like to see your Mom?"

Wiping back a tear, Jacob replied, "Yes-sir, I would. When she died, I liked to died myself. I ain't been worth a button since. I miss everythin' 'bout her. Her smile. Her hugs. The way she sang—like a lark—when she hung clothes out to dry on the line." He flashed a bashful smile. "I even miss her baked beans, 'n I hate baked beans."

Mountain took two giant steps to the cell and reached his hand through the bars, cupping the back of Jacob's head in his palm. Love that would melt a block of ice brimmed over from eyes that minutes before were set in steely bitterness.

"Son," he said, his lower lip quivering, "forgive me for turning you against God. Your dear mother was right all along. I just.... when she died I couldn't.... I was so angry, my head was so muddled. I wanted to hate someun' and that someun' was Him."

"I forgive you, Dad. It weren't your fault. I was angry, too."

"But you were a boy. That was three years and four months ago. It *was* my fault and I'm so sorry."

Jacob stepped up tight against the bars and the father and son hugged each other as best they could through the obstruction.

Seth had stepped closer, afraid what he was observing was an act. *Could Mountain actually have a heart?* he wondered.

Mountain looked at his son through watery eyes. "I've been a mean son-of-a-gun, a wretched man since your Ma died, Jacob. I prided myself on just how mean I could be. I don't want you to let any of that meanness settle on you—not now."

Jacob sobbed, "It won't, Dad."

Outside, the crowd shouted something. "Justice," perhaps.

"Sheriff," Mountain turned watery eyes toward Seth, "ain't

there nothin' you can do to save my boy? Justice ain't served by hangin' the boy."

Seth shook his head sadly. "It's not in my power. No longer, Mister Trimble. I'm very sorry."

Mountain turned to Francis and pleaded, "Preacher, is there somethin', anythin' you can do?"

Francis shrugged shoulders made heavy with grief. "Mister Trimble, I can do the best thing of all: send Jacob home to a place his Lord has been preparing for him for some two thousand years, a place where his Mom is waiting for him—and for you."

To Jacob, Francis said: "The Bible says that whoever believes in the Lord Jesus Christ and confesses so with his mouth will be saved."

"That's too simple, sir. I'm too much a sinner!" the boy exclaimed.

"Yes, it's too simple. Too simple for us to do to make ourselves worthy of salvation. But it's not too simple for God, Who directed it so. He wanted it so simple that no one would doubt it was a gift from Him. It's so simple that no man can boast of his salvation. No man can boast that he did this and that, built cathedrals to God and led so many to salvation, and therefore deserves salvation himself. We're not saved by works but by the grace of God.

"Scripture tells us that the 'wages of sin are death, but the gift of God is eternal life.' Not one person on this earth can boast that they earned salvation, so don't expect it of yourself, Jacob."

"So what *do* I do?"

"Do you believe in the Lord Jesus Christ?"

"Yup."

"Do you believe that He came from heaven and died for your sins?"

"Yup, ever since my Mom told me."

"Do you believe that God raised Him from the dead?"

"I sure do."

"Will you make Him Lord of your life?"

The lad smiled ever so slightly. "Yup, for what little's left of it."

"Then, Jacob, you are saved. And this very day you will see God Almighty face to face—and your Mom, too. There's no waiting line."

Jacob called to his father and Mountain pressed hard against the bars to again hug his son.

Seth stepped in. "It's time, Jacob—Mister Trimble."

Francis backed away and said softly to Seth, "Constable, may I say a few words to the crowd out there—afterwards."

Seth nodded assent.

It was a quick process, escorting Jacob to the gallows out in the public square. Mountain stayed behind in the jailhouse, unable to watch his son be hanged. Alongside the hangman, Jacob, his head high, stepped sprightly up the stairs. One would have thought he was going to a dance, or a wedding rather than his own execution.

When Jacob reached the top of the stairs Seth, who was standing at the bottom, faced the crowd. "Today we hang Jacob Winslow Trimble for the crime of horse theft, having been found guilty by a jury of his peers here in the Town of Burlington in the Commonwealth of Pennsylvania." He looked up at Jacob. "Do you have anything to say, young man?"

Jacob looked over the crowd. "Only this, sir: that I'm sorry for all the wrong I've done. I've been bad. I deserve this hangin'. And, Mister," he looked at a man standing in the front of the crowd, "I am surely sorry I stole your horse. In these parts that's nearly as bad as killin' someone, and I guess this hangin' is proof of that."

Francis looked on with pride at this young man whom he had just met. What a corner to turn in the climax of a person's life. What an epilogue awaited him! Francis recalled the last time he was able to speak with a prisoner awaiting hanging. The results were as dissimilar as they could be. When he came forth to the gallows, he roared like a bull in a net. He looked on every side, and shrieked for help; but all in vain. Oh, how awful! Francis had prayed with him and for him, but found how difficult it was to drench a hardened sinner with religion.

A moment later, Jacob fell through a trap door, out of sight, his neck broken by the hangman's rope. Sometimes these hangings took some time to accomplish their goal, but not with Jacob. Women and children gasped as Jacob fell out of sight. Some men groaned. The man whose horse Jacob had stolen lowered his head. *Is he contemplating if the punishment was equal to the crime?* Francis wondered.

As some in the crowd stood stunned and others turned to leave, Francis stepped to the front of the gallows and declared loudly, "Do not hang your head for Jacob Trimble. I say it again, don't hang your head!" The crowd turned back and looked intently on Francis. Many knew him, others guessed who he was by his commanding presence; by his long, flowing hair and the fact they knew he was to preach at the meeting hall that night.

"Jacob gave his life to the Lord just minutes ago in the jail cell," Francis continued. "Scripture tells us that as soon as we're absent from the body, we're present with the Lord. So Jacob has left this place of flesh and blood for a new residence in God's sweet heaven."

Francis looked over the people before him. "Jacob's namesake in the Bible experienced something we all need to experience. He wrestled with God and the Lord changed his name to Israel, which means 'one who has struggled with God.' God wants contenders, like the persistent widow, like Abraham, like Moses. While others slept, Jesus was always on the hilltop seeking His Father.

"In the end, Jacob Trimble finished wrestling with God and accepted that He indeed exists, that He indeed is Lord, that He indeed forgives sin, and that He indeed prepares a place in heaven for the repentant. No matter how bad your sin—even horse theft, even murder—God will forgive you if you truly, in your heart, repent and flee away from your sin and run toward Him.

"No servant can serve two masters. Those of you here today who are serving a master other than the Lord can change your destiny. Hell awaits you if you don't! It's a simple choice. Make the choice that Jacob Trimble made today!"

An hour had gone by, Jacob's body had been removed and the crowd had dispersed before the last person, a young woman with a scarf pulled tightly about her head, bowed before Francis, weeping at the goodness of a God who would forgive her adultery.

CHAPTER 7

Confronting Washington on Slavery

Richard Wright met Francis at the door of Richard Boardman's former house. Richard smiled broadly and crookedly at Francis, disregarded his dusty coat, and wrapped his arms around Francis in a bear hug.

"Frankie, my friend!"

"Welcome back to America, Richard." Francis returned Richard's smile and looked over his friend. It was early May 1785. Richard had been back and forth from England twice, this last time he had been gone for a year, and Francis had missed him immensely. It would be wonderful to catch up with him and get the news about friends and family in England directly from him. "You look to be faring well."

Richard cocked his head and his broad smile turned to a sheepish one. "Frankie, you were right. You were the only one of us who was. John and Charles Wesley. Rankin. We all misjudged the Revolution. The feeling back home now is that, if you had returned with the rest of us, the colonial followers would have felt abandoned in their greatest time of need, and, in all likelihood, would have gone to other churches, leaving the Methodist societies to disintegrate."

Francis lowered his eyes and nodded. "But I do understand your reasoning then. It appeared that it was like David versus Goliath. Impossible odds. But, thank God, the boy, while immature, had a strong faith in God. And the giant, not questioning his own ability to subdue this 'child,' discovered what the Bible tells us: 'Do not trust in chariots and horses but in the mighty arm of the Lord.'"

"We could not believe the reports we were hearing in England. Your analogy fits well. America was David—young and with a mere slingshot in his hand; and England was Goliath, armed with massive troops and mighty cannons."

Francis took off his coat, shook the dust from it and hung it on a peg by the door. "Well, I must admit, it did take more than one pebble to the monster's brow to bring him to his knees. And it has eaten up nearly a decade of our time."

Francis' eyes brightened. "But it did not completely stifle our work here, Richard."

He motioned toward the kitchen. "Let me tell you about it. Tea?"

Richard nodded. "I've got it brewing already, Frankie."

The two friends sat at a table in the kitchen. Francis picked up the conversation. "As a matter of fact, by standing with America, we stand in good stead with the new government. Doors are open that would not otherwise be open. And the doors of our meeting houses have stayed open that would otherwise have been shut."

"Praise God," Richard said.

"Yes, praise His name! And our membership, Richard, has grown—from six hundred when you and I landed here in Philadelphia, to more than fourteen thousand."

"That's amazing."

"Amazing, but only the beginning, now that you and the others who are coming will be able to fill the circuits we've created."

Francis and Richard were interrupted by a cough from the hall. Thomas Coke entered the room. "There'll be more than eighty of us here by next month, Frank."

Francis rose from his seat and shook the little man's hand. "Tom! Welcome back!"

"I'm back and I'm ready to ride, Frank."

"I am as well, Tom, but I would like one night in a fine bed before heading back out. I can't recall the last time I slept on feathers."

Coke laughed. "The vagaries of missionary work, Frank. But you might find our next 'mission' to be interesting."

Francis looked questioningly at Coke, and Coke responded. "We're going to visit General Washington and discuss the business of slavery."

"In Mount Vernon?"

"In Mount Vernon. It's May. He's at his estate to oversee planting season and recuperate from the war."

"Hallelujah!"

•••••

The next day, Francis and Coke were on their way, and four days later they rode onto Washington's estate, Mount Vernon. Oh, spectacular! It was set on a slope with views of the Potomac River and the Maryland shoreline to the east and the pastoral bowling green to the west, where the sun was on its downward arc. A magnificent place. A broad front porch was graced with eight pillars rising above the second-story windows, three small gables set above, and a widow's walk sitting atop the roof like a crown. What a regal home it was, a home befitting a king! In fact, Francis felt as though they were visiting the King of England. And, of course, General Washington could have been declared king of the new nation. Americans even tried to deify him. In later years, he reportedly was baffled and mortified by the Washington's Birthday Bash and its Birthnight Balls that people held around the republic.

Francis stepped down from Silver Fox.

John Wesley had declared the slave trade "that execrable sum of all villainies," and Coke and Francis agreed. Coke may have been a little man in stature, but he was a mighty man in the power of God. They went to meet with General Washington to ask him to sign a petition they had started and to use his influence to free the slaves. Francis was aware that Washington had been born into a world where slavery was accepted—a way of life for landowners. He was a boy when his father died and left him ten slaves and five hundred acres of land. When he married Martha, she brought more slaves with her, and they relied on that labor to operate their farm. Yet Coke and Francis had heard that Washington's stand on slavery had wavered, and they prayed for his support.

Francis looked up at the weathercock that stood atop the widow's walk. The wind was pushing it southward, and he wondered if that were a harbinger of defeat to them in their endeavor. Indeed, soon enough they had a hint of the conversation to come when they were greeted by two slaves who took their horses for them, to water and feed them while they visited with General Washington. Coke and Francis exchanged concerned looks as another slave opened the front doors for them and led them inside the house.

They entered the wide front doors to a central passage that ran from the front to the rear of the home, with doors opening off it both to the left and right and a graceful walnut staircase leading to the second floor. Pine paneling throughout the entryway created a rich feeling of warmth and welcome. This was obviously the main setting for entertaining guests.

The black woman who had led them inside spoke up. "This way, gentlemen, to the front parlor." They began to follow her to the room to their left when Washington called out from the top of the staircase, "No, Marcy. I'll show the gentlemen to my study."

Marcy acted surprised. Francis knew the front parlor was the customary place for social visits, for tea and coffee, for pleasantries. Washington's study was his personal sanctuary. Few were allowed there.

Washington reached the bottom of the stairs and extended his hand in welcome. Washington stood six-foot-two or three, weighed about two hundred pounds and possessed a strong and commanding presence. He was obviously at ease in his surroundings. Francis thought that, after a long, tedious and sometimes ferocious war, it must feel wonderful, in many ways, for Washington to be back at his home, with food and shelter now commonplace.

"Honored to have you visit," Washington said.

"It's our honor, General," Coke said.

Washington turned to Francis. "I've heard you preach, Mister Asbury. You stirred my heart and convicted my soul."

"Bless God, sir," Francis replied.

"Follow me, please."

Washington showed them through a small dining room and into a large room with several tall windows looking out onto the grounds of the estate. A large globe of the world stood near the middle of the room. An exquisite glassed-in, curved bookcase graced one wall. A shallow fireplace was centered on another curved wall, surrounded by maple paneling.

Evidences of the man inside the man were everywhere. Three muskets stood against one corner. A telescope and well-worn Bible occupied a small table by a window. What appeared to be records of a corn crop were sprawled on a draftsman's table, perhaps a holdover from his early career as a surveyor. A secretary's desk stood before another window, and what appeared to be Washington's office desk commanded another wall; its roll-top was closed and built onto its top was a small glass-encased bookcase with exquisite carved woodwork and filled with books.

"Please," Washington said, gesturing toward chairs at which to sit. They all sat down.

"Thank you for seeing us, General," Coke began. "Our journey is specifically to discuss our petition to pass laws against slavery."

"We were under the impression, sir, that you were now opposed to slavery," Francis said. "It appears we may have been mistaken?"

"This is difficult," Washington said. "I must confess I feel as if I'm in a salad bowl, being tossed about here and there concerning this issue. The older I get the more opposed I am to this peculiar institution. On one hand, I realize it's immoral and unjust. And yet, as you see around us, at the same time, the more slaves I have makes for a complex problem for me. I need the manpower simply in order to run my five farms that are on this plantation. Three-fourths of my slaves work in the fields. But, many of the other men are trained in such crafts as milling, blacksmithing, coopering, shoemaking and carpentry. Others are boatmen, coachmen, or field hands. And while many of our women work in the dairy, laundry, kitchen, or in the fields, others are taught spinning, weaving and sewing.

"You see, I dislike the idea of slavery, but its reality is, pragmatically, the rule of the land. There simply are not enough free men in the Republic available for hire to run this estate."

Washington steepled his fingers. "Bishop Asbury—Bishop Coke—I have thought about this, and prayed about it for countless hours, and it's more complex than simply making the practice of slavery illegal. Despite my own personal quandary in terms of available labor, I believe if we pass this petition into law we'll cause a division between the Northern states and Southern states that our fledgling country would not survive."

"Sir," Francis said, "this petition certainly would cause strain between the states, but it could also change the course of this new nation. And adding your support could truly make a significant difference for this new nation and its future—especially if you would speak publicly for its passage."

"I have personally conveyed my views face to face with most of the great men of Virginia," Washington responded. Francis couldn't read if it was impatience or defensiveness that he read in Washington's voice. "I don't believe it proper for me to sign your petition, but if the Assembly takes it into consideration I'll signify my sentiments to that body by letter."

Coke hung his head, but Francis held Washington's gaze. "General Washington," he said, "Massachusetts emancipated slaves two years ago, Rhode Island and Connecticut last year. We understand that strong opposition to our petition exists in Virginia and the Carolinas. But abolition is inevitable, and you can be either on the right side of it or the wrong."

Washington leaned forward in his chair, drawing closer to Francis. Anguish was etched on his face. "I personally will never again purchase a slave, Bishop Asbury. And it's among my primary wishes to see some plan adopted by which slavery in this country may be abolished by slow, sure, and imperceptible degrees.

"But—but I can not at this time add my signature to your entreaty."

Francis nodded his head and replied solemnly, "We intend to continue these petitions, year by year, until they are passed into law. And until that day, General, my statement to slave owners who'll not free their slaves is this: 'Ladies and gentlemen, beware, for God will depart from you.'"

Washington reacted as though he had been pierced by a bayonet and rocked back in his chair. Measuring his words for a moment, he said, "Oh, my dear Bishop. I pray you're not correct. And more so, I pray that the Sovereign will be watching over you if, indeed, you preach such a thing to the masses—especially those in Virginia and southward."

Expecting to be escorted in all haste from the Washington mansion, Francis began to rise from his chair. But Washington held up a hand in protest. "Dear sir, I meant no harm, merely a warning of your reception in the South. In fact, I hope that you and Doctor Coke can spend the night here with Martha and me. She's a staunch churchgoer and would love to have you dine with us and stay the night, at least."

Coke spoke first. "Thank you, General. We'd love to dine with you and your dear wife. But then we must be off since we have an engagement at Annapolis in the morning."

•••••

Abigail Brackett stepped before Francis with a tray containing muffins and cups filled with steaming tea. He took a muffin in one hand and a cup and saucer in another, thanked her, and took a bite from the muffin.

"Delicious, Abigail!"

"Thank you."

Sam and Nicholas joined in the treat.

"The Lord has led you into contact with many of our founding fathers," Abigail said.

"Yes, I've been entertained by governors and mayors,

spoken to most state legislatures, and preached to the House of Representatives in Washington, but the Lord has a way of humbling His servants," Francis laughed. "Two days after dining with General Washington, for instance."

That trip stayed fresh in Francis' mind. He and Thomas Coke held successful meetings in Annapolis after their conference with Washington. Then they headed to western Virginia and South Carolina together to spread their opinions about slavery and call for all Methodists to free their Negroes.

A near-full moon shed good light upon the woods that night. It was about midnight and Francis and Coke were quiet, caught in their own solitary thoughts. Francis had been praying for his mother, that she would know God's protection and receive His provision. He sent her most of what he earned as bishop, yet was concerned that that wasn't enough. What did that say about his faith? Didn't God love her even more than he?

Suddenly they were out of the woods and in the barnyard of a man named Ainsworth. In fact, Ainsworth was emerging from his barn, holding a lantern before him. Hearing them, he turned to see who it was, perhaps concerned that they were Indians. Squinting into the distance, he called, "Asbury?"

Francis replied, "Yes."

Ainsworth turned back to the barn and called, "Jag! Koby!" Waving a hand toward Francis and Coke, he hissed, "Sic!" Suddenly, two shadows emerged on a run from the barn and headed straight at the two preachers.

Francis, and Coke behind him, turned their horses to an angle and rode at a gallop toward the road to town. Yapping non-stop, the dogs bit at their horses' legs. *They really love us here, Lord!,* Francis thought, half laughing, considering the strange juxtaposition of events—from meeting with General Washington to being driven from a Christian-hating farmer's home.

A distant whistle called the dogs off their chase, and Francis and Coke were able to amble on toward their destination. That night their bed was a few flea-infested deerskins on a floor of a widow's porch. Their poor horses got no corn, and next morning they had to swim across the Monongahela River. It took the two men and beasts ten hours to travel the twenty miles, finally arriving, exhausted, in Clarksburg. There they lodged with Colonel George Jackson, and a fatigued Francis lay in a comfortable bed, thinking how America, even after all these years, compared so poorly to his old home in England.

How glad he was to have this comfortable bed tonight. And the company of Jackson, a war hero and lawyer who was active in the politics of the Commonwealth of Virginia, was exceptional. But, as often as not, beds were even worse than a plain, clean plank to lie on and, often, where the beds were in a bad state the floors were worse. In Virginia, the gnats were almost as troublesome as the mosquitoes in the lowlands of the seacoast. Oh, how much work this country required to make it tolerable!

After a couple of days preaching in Clarksburg, Francis and Coke rode another twenty-two miles to Lowell, Virginia, driven by awful thunder, wind and rain. Dripping wet, they found refuge at Colonel James Graham's two-story log home. Colonel Graham and his wife, Florence, received them, poor strangers, with great kindness, and treated them hospitably. Indeed, this was not new for the Grahams, whose home also served as a fortress to protect the settlers from the ever-present danger of Indian attack.

That evening, Francis was stricken with symptoms that had killed his Grandfather Francis Asbury. Sinking into a down mattress and covered with a down comforter offered up by Florence, Francis lay ill for several days. Outside, the rain pelted the cabin during that time, preventing travel even if he were healthy.

It seemed an eternity. Sweat pouring from his body, weariness taking the form of a weight holding him down like an anvil, he dozed on and off. He was unable to focus enough to read, so Coke read to him from the Bible the several hours a day that John Wesley required.

In the midst of his sickness he looked into eternity with some pleasure. He could give up the church, the college and the schools. *Ah, to see my Lord face to face!* But, there was one drawback: What would his detractors and mistaken friends say? That he had offended God, of course, and the Lord had taken him away.

Finally, the rains stopped, the roads were passable, and Francis felt well enough to travel a mile to town to hear Brother Richard Whatcoat preach. It was the perfect sermon for his state of mind. Whatcoat declared, "The kingdom of God is not in word but in power, not in sentiments or forms, but in the convincing, converting, regenerating, sanctifying power of God."

Power to save. Power to deliver from sin. Power to heal! But Francis struggled within himself. He could preach a good sermon. He could pray a good prayer. Why did he so often succumb to illness? True, his wasn't a normal life, trudging about along the Atlantic seaboard three hundred sixty days a year, drenched by rain, blistered by heat, fending off icy cold, sucking in malaria vapors, exposed to tens of thousands of people—and, therefore, the illnesses of some—each year.

He and Coke settled back that evening with the Grahams and their son and daughter. It was the first since they had arrived that Francis felt well enough to hold a civil conversation. But what a conversation it was! Colonel Graham told his daughter, a pretty, long-haired brunette, to sit at his side as he related his story, and he proceeded to weave the most amazing tale of tenacity and God's grace. He and Florence were the perfect example of the biblical encouragement to continue bringing your request before the Lord, not giving up, and sticking your finger in the eye of discouragement.

Eight years before, in the spring of 1777, Shawnee Indians attacked the Graham home before dawn one night. When it was over, their ten-year-old boy, John, their neighbor and friend, Ted McDonald, and their faithful servant, Sharp, were dead; and their seven-year-old daughter, Elizabeth, was missing.

In the midst of the darkness and confusion, Colonel Graham was able to load his musket only twice and, with one shot, thought he wounded one of the Indians as they ran from the home.

By a miracle, their twelve-year-old son, William, was alive, because he had been taken ill and was not sleeping with the other children but was in the outhouse when the attack occurred. The

Grahams wept over the fate of the dead, but wondered where Elizabeth was. Had the Indians taken her to kill her? Was her mangled body left in the woods or drowned in the creek? Was she alive but lost, fleeing from wild animals that could devour her? The Grahams were caught in the middle of fear and hope. If she was a captive, was she being tortured? Raped? At least if she were dead, she would not have to endure such abuse. Gloom and despair usually prevailed in this struggle of the mind. And yet, James and Florence carried on an assault on the gates of heaven, asking God to spare the life of their child.

James spent eight years searching the territories for hundreds of miles around. Finally, just two weeks before Francis' and Thomas' arrival, his inquiries were rewarded. A miracle! People in Kentucky had heard of a young white girl, a teenager, living in a nearby Shawnee village.

Through an Indian agent who acted as a go-between, Colonel Graham offered to trade blankets and trinkets to the tribe for Elizabeth's release.

The girl, now fifteen years old and a slave to the Shawnees, screamed in joy when she saw her father enter the Indian camp. The fear that seemed to howl at the door of his mind as he approached the Shawnee chief battled with the joyous expectation of saving his daughter. But the chief, for some reason, agreed to the exchange.

Concerned that the Indians would chase after them, Colonel Graham was inspired to have his friends put all their horses' horseshoes on backward for the journey home in order to confuse any pursuers.

He and his friends put their lives at risk, but he said he felt they were in the Lord's hands.

What a glorious story.

"Find favor with God and you'll find favor with man," Francis said to Colonel Graham. Graham simply smiled, and hugged Elizabeth beside him.

"Yes, sir, and this is the result. Our Elizabeth. Nearly all grown up; a young woman. We missed her growing up, until now, but we know the Lord was watching over her."

Francis grinned at the girl. "I suppose your story is going to be told for a very long time, young lady." Her face beamed in response.

Francis thought of the ordeals that child had overcome. How was it that he, Francis Asbury, should complain of his days fighting gnats, his nights fending off fleas and men like Ainsworth hissing their dogs after him. These were agitations of little consequence.

•••••

Finding himself well enough to travel the next day, Francis urged Thomas to continue their journey to preach the end of slavery. They decided to split up, Thomas traveling eastward through Virginia while Francis rode southward into North and South Carolina. They would meet in a month at the home of the parson of Parish Church of Norfolk Towne, Virginia, which had been partially fire-gutted when the British burned the town in 1776.

Francis found himself a few days later in a playhouse owned by a fellow Methodist, who had asked him to preach there. He had not yet reached North Carolina, but was in the southern reaches of Virginia. Hundreds of townspeople filled the seats; others stood along the wall.

Francis squared his shoulders. He sensed tension, perhaps even animosity, but he could not understand it since this crowd didn't know what he was about to preach. Or had his message preceded him here?

After his opening prayer, Francis lit squarely upon his topic. "When the colonies declared separation from England, our Declaration of Independence stated unequivocally that the truths were self-evident that men 'are endowed by their Creator with certain unalienable rights, that among these are life, liberty and the pursuit of happiness.' Is this not right?"

The walls of the playhouse reverberated a hearty "Amen!" This was a people who had recently liberated themselves from a slave master in King George III. They could relate to living a life entirely at the behest of one man—detached and disinterested—working a hard life only to pay taxes to a king, a dictator, with no end, no deliverance in sight.

"The Declaration of Independence continues, 'to secure these rights, governments are instituted among men, deriving their just powers from the consent of the governed.'" Francis looked around the rows of seats. "Whose consent is that?"

"Of the governed!" came a loud response.

"The Declaration goes on to say that when a long train of abuses and usurpations reduces the citizens under absolute despotism, it's their right, it's their duty, to throw off such government."

A loud "hoorah!" came from most of the men in attendance.

"....and to provide new guards for their future security. 'Such has been the patient sufferance of these colonies,'" Francis added, "'and such is now the necessity which constrains them to alter their former systems of government.'"

He looked keenly at several of those before him. Would they comprehend what he was about to tell them, the parallel he was drawing? "Today I ask you to look at your plight at the hands of a despotic king and uncaring Parliament and compare it to the predicament of another people."

The eyes upon him became questioning. What was Asbury about to tell them? Francis hesitated and prayed silently that the Lord would unstop stubborn ears and soften any hearts of stone.

"Just as you were all serfs to King George through his many taxations dominated in your elemental pursuit of life, liberty and happiness, so too are the slaves here in America."

There was a hesitation as the crowd absorbed his statement, then a few "Amens" emanated from the group.

"They have no rights, no representation in our fledgling state legislatures."

There was silence on the lips of many who, moments before, were vocal.

"Americans declared, and fought for, an end to despotism. Will we now—in order to pick our fields of cotton and farm products—

deny the end of despotism that exists in the system of slavery?"

Half the room of people—perhaps more—agreed with him, it appeared. Some of the others may have also agreed but were afraid to add voice to that opinion.

"We're commanded to love the Lord our God and our neighbors as ourselves," Francis continued. "Who is our neighbor? Is it the person sitting next to you? The person across the way, standing at the back door? Is it the mayor of your town, the attorney for your estate, the shop owner who sells you yard goods, the blacksmith who attends your horses? Who was the neighbor for the Good Samaritan? In the Samaritan's case, if you listen to and heed our Lord Jesus, you'll agree that we're to love those whom we don't even know.

"Then I ask you, pulling up all your conviction like a tight coat around your shoulders, look inside yourselves and answer the question: Are not slaves your neighbors? And should not slaves have the same right to liberty as you—free men and free women? Liberated from the tyranny of the British Parliament?"

A mixture of responses echoed through the playhouse. Joy and agreement were ablaze on many a face. Anger and dismay were etched on others. Several men stood up from their seats and sprang toward the rear door as if the hall were on fire.

The next morning, as Francis readied to step up into Silver Fox's saddle, a full two dozen men, six abreast, walked determinedly toward him. Francis could not mistake the animosity in their bearing. And they appeared to march like an army—a small army, but an army indeed. Thankfully, he saw no ammunition, no muskets or cannon. But if looks could kill....

"Gentlemen!" he greeted them.

"Preacher," one man clipped off the word as if he did not want it to linger too long on his tongue, "we want a word with you."

"Certainly."

Francis measured the speaker. He didn't recall his face from the crowd the previous night. He was a full-bearded man, a large man who had apparently grown from a horse load to a cart load. He was perhaps fifty years old. Dressed in a fine coat, wearing a fine hat, sporting fine, shiny boots, and carrying what looked to be a horse whip—probably a very fine horse whip at that—he appeared to be a man of means. The men beside and behind him were surely a mixture, though, of wealthy, somewhat wealthy, and medium income. Some were determined, some uneasy. Some ready for fisticuffs without debate, some for talk. Some dragging others along, some being dragged along.

"Last night you called for an end to slavery."

"Yes."

"Cease and desist."

"Cease and desist what, sir?"

"Cease and desist seeking such a thing!"

Anger. It as an easy emotion for this man, Francis thought.

"But it's something I believe we must do for our new republic to be able to survive, sir," Francis said, locking his eyes on this man.

"Slavery is to the trade of the country, as the soul is to the body," the man declared.

"Then that soul is destined for the bleak obscurity of hell."

"Abolish slavery and we fail!"

"Keep it and you fail."

"Keep it and we're able to maintain our economy!"

"Keep it and the same God who blessed your Revolution will abandon your economy."

"He blessed our Revolution while we held slaves." The man thought he had Francis cornered in this line of thought.

"One tyrant held a loaded gun to the head of all Americans. With slavery, the tyrants are not kings and they don't lord it over entire colonies. The tyrants are slave owners and they lord it over mere households. But a tyrant is a tyrant, sir. Be sure of that."

Francis held the man in an iron grip with a fierce look. "And if the Almighty allowed His chosen people, the Hebrews, to be defeated by the Babylonians because the Hebrews abandoned God, be assured that He will allow self-willed men who disobey His commands to be handed over to the enemy of men. That enemy, sir, is Satan. And so, if I preach an end to slavery, and you are a slave owner yourself, I preach for your salvation."

"Try to preach here again on this topic, and you'll be the one needing salvation!"

Francis shrugged, nodded to the man, and mounted Silver Fox. Looking down at them, he said matter-of-factly: "I must listen to God and not men. I'll preach what He puts on my heart to preach—threats or no threats. But I will give you this warning, gentlemen: Lay a hand on me and beware the thunderbolt of God."

With that, Francis rode out of town. And as he left, he thought that some of those men could be spiritual cousins of church leadership in America, some of whom themselves were slave owners.

•••••

Village after village, as the summer progressed, Francis preached against slavery. Village after village, he was met with a mixture of acceptance and anger edging on fury. But Francis met the worst of all menaces in Georgia, where slaves were said to comprise half the population.

Standing in front of a town hall on a Sunday morning, Francis had an audience of two hundred, perhaps.

"We're to be slaves to Christ—and Him alone," Francis declared in ending his sermon. "I speak to all who hear my voice this morning, if you have slaves, set them free. If you don't have slaves, convince your neighbor who does to set his free."

An older man, dressed in finery, with an expensive hat indeed topping the picture to perfection, and standing in the midst of several black people, stepped forward from the periphery of the crowd. "Christ Himself never spoke against slavery," the man declared, pointing a cane at Francis, "and the apostle Paul admonished slaves to obey their masters."

"Get your facts straight if you intend to inject God's Word into a matter, sir," Francis responded. "*Slavery* is a potent word today and we must be careful with it. Would you say that the Cabinet of the new American government will be *slaves* to our new President when he's elected?"

"Of course not."

"And yet," Francis said, "that is one of the uses of the word *slave* in the Bible. The Hebrew word *ebed* denotes not only an actual slave working in the household or in producing something for sale, it also indicates a person in a subordinate position, usually in regard to a king or his high-ranking officials. *Ebed* was used meaning 'a slave, or servant of God.' In Exodus, Leviticus, Samuel and Ezra—in all these books—Abraham, Isaac, Jacob, David, the kings and prophets are regularly called 'slaves of God,' while the Israelites called themselves slaves to the prophets and Moses. Ruth referred to herself as a slave girl of Boaz.

"In Genesis chapter twenty, Abimelech, king of Gerar, called up his slaves and told them his dream. Do you think these 'slaves' were laborers in the field? No, they were apparently royal courtiers and officials.

"In Second Chronicles, when Amaziah ascended the throne of Judah, he executed his 'slaves' who had murdered his father, the former king. These 'slaves' were certainly royal dignitaries."

"Even kings, sir," Francis fixed the man with his eyes, "were referred to as 'servants' or 'slaves' of more powerful kings."

"Kings of old aren't plantation owners of modern times," the man shot back, stepping through the crowd toward Francis.

"You know not history, nor the history of slavery," Francis said.

"Ha! And how many have you owned?" the man responded.

"None and I shan't—ever," Francis said. "But you miss my point. Slavery in Roman times was far different from slavery today. So different, in fact, that some men sold their wives, or children, or elderly family member as debt slaves. Some even sold themselves into slavery in the hope of becoming stewards of noblemen or imperial treasuries."

"Bah! Rubbish! I'll believe that on Saint Geoffrey's Day!"

"What's that?"

"Since there's no saint by that name, it means tomorrow-come-never."

"Really? Then you haven't heard of Pallas, scion of a noble Arcadian family, who sold himself into slavery so that he might become steward to a woman of the imperial family and then earned his way to minister of finance for Emperor Claudius?"

The man shook his head.

"Or of Melissus, a teacher and author who flourished so much as a slave that he received a commission from Augustus himself?"

The man, now in the front row of people standing before Francis, shook his head.

Francis put his hands to his hips. "How about Trimalchio, who gained fame running a great business for his master?"

"Names you've made up of whole cloth!" the man declared.

"Then I assume you're more aware of Joseph, the son of Jacob, grandson of Isaac and great-grandson of Abraham."

"Of course."

"He was called a 'slave' but ruled his master's house and eventually managed the entire country of Egypt for the king. Have you given that kind of rein to any of your slaves, sir?"

"Of course not."

"You're familiar with Daniel?" Francis' eyebrow raised. The man scowled.

Francis continued, "King Nebuchadnezzar of Babylon brought Daniel and his friends Shadrach, Meshach and Abednego—all 'slaves' captured in war—into the palace, fed and clothed them and had them taught in the language and literature of the Babylonians. Eventually, Nebuchadnezzar gave them charge over huge portions of his kingdom."

The wealthy man simply stared at Francis, apparently dumbfounded as to what to say.

Francis continued: "And Abraham entrusted a slave to be his steward, gave him charge of his entire household, and even charged him with traveling to a foreign country and choosing a bride for Isaac."

The man took two steps forward and nearly hollered, "That was then! This is now! Slaves are slaves!"

"No." Francis stood firm. "Slavery today can not even be compared to slavery in the ancient world. Within all the periods of history, victorious Egyptian, Persian, Mesopotamian, Hittite and Oriental rulers carried away great numbers of the conquered nations as captives, but turned only a few of them into slaves. They allowed most to settle on the land as palace and temple serfs, and others to remain on their own lands and to work those lands, paying an annual tax to the conqueror."

"Those slaves and our slaves are not the same!" the man replied.

"Sir," Francis said, "you're the one, are you not, who tried to instill the Bible into this debate by saying that Christ Himself never spoke against slavery and that Paul admonished slaves to obey their masters.

"What you say is correct: those slaves and our slaves today are not the same. So you can not use the apostle Paul's words to justify your actions, can you? And, tell me, if the gospel will tolerate slavery, what will it *not* authorize?!"

The man harrumphed, and started to turn and walk away.

Francis interrupted him, "Are you a Christian, sir?"

The man stopped and looked, unblinking, at Francis. "Yes."

"Then you lay claim to the pureness and holiness that comes with following Christ?"

"I certainly do."

As Francis and his antagonist parried, the crowd watched and listened carefully, turning to form a circle, with the two men in the middle. It appeared to Francis somewhat like a miniature of the Roman Colosseum. Francis and his adversary were being offered up in a battle for the minds of the crowd. They were as red meat, thrust through with a sword, battered with a bludgeon, depending on cunning, wile and pure power. The Roman centurion was missing; King Herod was nowhere in sight; nevertheless, Francis could feel the prayer of many in the crowd supporting him, hoping for a winning blow, while others—pragmatists, they would call themselves—were succumbing to what they felt was "realism" and were pulling for the other man's victory.

Francis could hear the Holy Spirit: "Your struggle is not against flesh and blood but against the rulers, authorities and powers of this dark world and against the spiritual forces of evil in the heavenly realms." *Amen, Lord.* He looked at the man and asked, "How many slaves do you own, sir?"

"One hundred forty-two."

"Do your slaves live in your house?"

"Some of them do—if they're cooks and housekeepers—and some of them are here with me....," the man pointed toward a half-dozen black men and women at the rear of the circle, "because, Mister Asbury, I believe it my duty to introduce them to the Almighty."

"So, you are about God's business."

"Yes."

"Then, while you're about the Lord's business, why not introduce them to freedom and liberty, sir?"

"I treat my slaves well."

"Would you say you treat them as well as pagans did their slaves in ages past?"

"Absolutely."

"In first-century Babylon slaves were paid the equivalent of what adult hired workers received. Enterprising slaves operated businesses, were engaged in trade and could own land, houses and other possessions. In courts, they were treated equally with free men and could appear as witnesses and plaintiffs as well as defendants. Does that sound like the treatment you afford your slaves, sir?"

"Th-there m-must be a, an order to things. Th-there m-must be a—a—a—"

"A hierarchy?"

"Yes, hierarchy."

"You're at the top of that hierarchy?"

The man nodded.

"And your slaves are at the bottom of that hierarchy?"

"My slaves are well-treated, sir." The man turned to his slaves and motioned them to come to him. Turning to Francis and sweeping an arm toward his slaves, he asked, "Do you see a bruise on any of them?"

"I do not."

"Do you detect fear in any of them?"

"I can't see into their hearts, sir. Only God can."

The man looked at his slaves. "Are you afraid of me?"

They shook their heads in unison.

The man turned to Francis. "You see? No bruises, no fear...."

"And no freedom," Francis finished. "Sir, do you believe in the Golden Rule?"

The man hesitated, calculating the cost of his answer.

Francis pressed, "It says, 'Do unto others as you would have them do unto you.'"

"I know what it says!" The man was angry, but Francis sensed it was anger like that when you are shown a mistake in your way; an anger that bears with it responsibility that you must change, like it or not; an anger that Francis prayed was working the magic of God in the man's heart.

Nevertheless, the man turned on his heel and stalked off, pulling his hat down tight to his ears, stuffing one hand in his coat pocket while parting the crowd with the cane he held in the other. His slaves dutifully followed after him. The reaction from the crowd was curious. Francis sensed many, tense in the face of the confrontation, were exhaling for the first time in a minute, while others, thinking of their own slaves, were grumbling to themselves in the same manner that their neighbor was as he left the assembly.

Francis held up his right hand to draw the people's attention. "Friends, slavery would not exist if there were no buyers of slaves. Consequently, every buyer encourages the slave trade— and becomes partaker of the notorious guilt of it. Yes, there's guilt enough to spread around, like butter on bread—on both sides of the ocean. Here, the buyers. There, the sellers. Some Africans will sell their own children and neighbors. But we need not be complicit in their sin by attending their marketplace! By putting those human beings to work in our fields for no wages! By treating God's creatures as if they were oxen or field horses, or worse!"

A combination of ire and pity washed over Francis. *Christians doing such a thing! Putting their souls in eternal jeopardy!* "The Bible tells us 'A worker is worthy of his wages,'" he continued. "What of this notion? How do we fairly address this declaration from the Lord? By keeping people in servitude their entire lives?

"I declare again: Let mankind all be slaves to Christ, but let none of us be slaves to one another in the fashion that we do it here today. Let our new country begin its history by declaring freedom for all its inhabitants. And if the government is too afraid to do so, let us individually, before the eyes of God our Creator, do so."

"Hear, hear," came a scattering of responses. But Francis could sense an undercurrent of tension and apprehension, a tightly controlled hostility that breathed like a living being amidst the crowd. He repeated to himself, *Your battle is not against flesh and blood...."*

Feeling an urge to address the beast of fear that oppressed many of his congregation—fear of economic woes and even fear of change itself—Francis pressed on. "It must feel threatening, like another assault at the end of our long war with England, to face the possibility of harm to the economy, including the economy of some of your homes and businesses as well as the plantations. But in order to build a house that will stand, you must build it on a strong foundation. If a foundation of your economy is slavery, then that foundation is rotten. And if that foundation is rotten, you must rebuild it.

"You want to be scripturally sound as well as structurally sound. The Word says, 'Unless the Lord build the house they labor in vain who build it.'"

Recalling how this long season of fighting slavery had played out, Francis came back from his memories to the present and looked around at Sam and Abigail Brackett, little Thomas and Nicholas. "I commended the Quakers for their activities on behalf of the slaves and said the Methodists must come to the same praiseworthy position, or forfeit their spiritual crown. 'Deal it a mortal blow!' I bellowed then, and now as well. Alas, slavery is still with us, is it not?"

They all nodded solemnly.

•••••

After two months of traveling Georgia and the Carolinas, Francis rode north to meet with Coke. In Deer Creek, Virginia, he stayed at the home of Henry Watters whose father, William, was the first Native American to become a regular itinerant Methodist preacher. William had just bought a farm near McLean, Virginia, and relocated, and was determined to return to active ranks the next year, 1786. In the meantime, Henry, Samuel Litten and other Methodists in the area were wonderful hosts for three days of preaching. Many Friends also attended the meetings—black and white together—and Francis felt great freedom in the Spirit of God as he spoke pointedly and separately to each one.

Oh, the Lord had done great things for these people, notwithstanding the weakness of the instrument, Francis thought. *Men who neither feared God, nor regarded man—swearers, liars, cock fighters, card players, horse racers, drunkards—became new men, filled with the praises of God. It was the Lord's work and marvelous to behold!*

It was here that Francis learned that Coke and colleague James O'Kelley had been flogged by a mob after preaching for an end to slavery.

"They were fortunate they came off with whole bones," Francis said, looking around the cozy group sitting in front of the Brackett fireplace. Suddenly he was back in 1809, these memories just that, memories. Tom Coke—that wonderful, warm man of God. After the famous Christmas Conference, the two of them had partnered in God's work in America.

In theory, Coke and Francis shared equal power over the years. In reality, Coke's many absences from America left Francis in charge. Francis guessed Tom had crossed the Atlantic Ocean more than a dozen times, and had spoken of establishing another mission in India.

O'Kelley was another matter. After a warm and devoted friendship at first, conflict defined his relationship with Francis. Since Francis had won over the hearts of colonial leaders and Wesley had sent back his missionaries, Francis had re-established a number of circuits. And, acting under the Wesleyan "discipline," he had done so in a unilateral manner. O'Kelley and others railed at him, calling him a dictator. *But how better do it?* Francis wondered. *By committee? Let everyone haggle over who was given which circuit? That debate could go on and on, without resolution. Committees are the bane of efficiency and accomplishment. The Pilgrims would still be waiting on the docks of Europe if they had formed a committee to oversee their departure.*

And, if one person complained of his circuit and won designation to another circuit, what of the preacher assigned to that other circuit?

Francis knew O'Kelley made a good point—that Francis was a dictator and that circuit riders should have more say on what circuits they rode—but he thought his own reasoning trumped it.

O'Kelley and others declared that Francis played favorites. "Well, this is true," he had answered. "I **am** partial toward those willing to face the tough life outside the city."

Francis had told many a man that he wanted him to go to the rural districts, and he would say, "Here am I. Send Joe Jones!" That was a poor imitation of the Prophet Isaiah.

On December 25, 1792, the day of Francis' permanent appointment, the matter bubbled over at the Methodist Conference. O'Kelley made his point and some others agreed; Francis wanted unity, but could not agree to have the rules and government of the church trampled under foot.

Francis learned that O'Kelley, who was the presiding elder of his district, had planned to heckle Francis from the floor and try to entangle him in contradictory explanations, but when the conference opened, Francis was ill and couldn't attend. Coke took charge and read aloud a letter to the attendees from Francis:

"My Dear Brethren: Let my absence give you no pain—Doctor Coke presides. I'm happily excused from assisting to make laws by which I myself am to be governed. I have only to obey and execute." Seeing Francis' humility, the vast majority of those attending agreed with his stance.

In the midst of the fray, a young minister, Joshua Marsden, spoke up: "Methodists here in America should glory in having such a man as Bishop Asbury preside at our head. He is a man of integrity, diligence and zeal!"

Marsden straightened himself and looked about the full meetinghouse. "Bishop Asbury is one of those very few men whom nature forms in no ordinary mold, gentlemen. His mind is stamped with a certain greatness and originality that lifts him far above the merely learned man and fits him to be great without science, and venerable without titles."

His eyes flashed. "Is there one of you—even you, Mister O'Kelley—who doubts Bishop Asbury has a profound and penetrating knowledge of men; that he looks into character as one looks into a clear stream in order to discover the bottom? Yet he does not use this penetration toward unworthy purposes. He has one end in view, and one end only. That end is worthy of the dignity of an angel. That end is the salvation of souls by the furthering of the gospel into parts where God has not before ventured His ambassadors."

The entire hall was silent, struck by the candor of their young colleague.

"Does anyone here work harder, labor longer, travel more extensively, preach more often than Bishop Asbury?"

Heads simply shook in the negative.

"Of course not!" Marsden kept on his argument. "He pursues the most difficult course as most men do their pleasures. I've seen him so enfeebled by sickness and so weary with exhaustion that we had to strap him to his horse! I've seen him not able to stand to preach, nor kneel to pray! And yet he has gone on. Who here has done so?"

Not a hand was raised.

"To all that bear any resemblance to a polished and pleasing life, Bishop Asbury is dead," he continued. "And yet, if he wanted, he could sleep every night in the soft beds of this country's rich and famous, instead of the hard ground of the forest or a dusty cabin. He could taste the delicacies of the rich instead of hardened beef jerky and water from a flowing stream. No, he knows nothing about pleasing the flesh at the expense of duty. It appears he is blind to all worldly attractions! Am I not right?"

Heads nodded throughout the room.

"I have been in his presence on a variety of occasions and can testify that prayer is the seasoning of all his avocations, whether meal or business, and it's the benediction to all he takes in hand."

Marsden then looked fiercely about him. "And here, in the midst of an attempted rebellion of sorts, I must say that I once heard him preach upon union and brotherly love, and it was the greatest I ever heard upon that subject."

With that, Marsden returned to his seat, to pats on his shoulder from all those around him.

In the end, O'Kelley walked out of the conference with a half dozen of those in attendance. O'Kelley and his followers kept the Methodist name for another five or six years, calling themselves The Republican Methodists. "Republican," which they were to this very day, a decade later.

Francis struggled with the bitterness he felt over the rift, but thought of Paul and Barnabas. Going their separate ways assuredly meant many more souls being saved because they probably reached twice as many people with the gospel than if they had remained together. O'Kelley was a strong man of faith and his fruits would undoubtedly be many. Francis knew one thing: O'Kelley and Tom Coke could thank God alone that they survived their flogging.

He recalled Paul's soulful cry in the third chapter of Philippians: "I want to know Christ and the power of His resurrection and the fellowship of sharing in His sufferings, becoming like Him in His death, and so, somehow, to attain to the resurrection from the dead."

And the Apostle Peter joined the chorus in the fourth chapter of his first epistle, saying: "Therefore, since Christ suffered in his body, arm yourselves also with the same attitude, because he who has suffered in his body is done with sin. As a result, he does not live the rest of his earthly life for evil human desires, but rather for the will of God."

In a way, Francis was jealous of their flogging. Then, as a pang of his habitual pleurisy pierced his chest, he reconsidered. His own sufferings were seldom inflicted by man, but they were nevertheless sufferings, indeed.

Sam Brackett stood to his feet and stretched. "Francis, Nicholas," he nodded to the two men, "it's time I'm off to bed. I hope to get a third cut of hay into the barn in the next couple of days, so I have to get to it early in the morning. But I certainly want to hear the rest of your story, Francis. Can you continue after the church services tomorrow?"

Francis nodded assent.

CHAPTER 8

Treacherous Western Wilderness

The next morning was a Monday, but the Scarborough meetinghouse was nevertheless full to the walls at 5:30 in the morning when Robert Matthews prayed for God to speak words of wisdom and encouragement through Francis.

The sun had not yet risen over the trees to the east, and candlelight dimly lighted the large room, so Francis relied on memory to quote scripture.

"The apostle Paul told Timothy in his second epistle to his spiritual son, that 'In a large house there are articles not only of gold and silver, but also of wood and clay. Some are for noble purposes and some for ignoble.' He said, 'If a man cleanses himself from the latter (the ignoble), he will be an instrument for noble purposes, made holy, useful to the Master and prepared to do any good work.'"

Francis looked over the faces of these pioneers. They were trappers, farmers, and a few were fishermen. They were rugged, hardened by strenuous work, daily facing back-breaking tasks just to put food on their tables. They were simple people, though most of them were literate. They were people who, by necessity, lived with fear; after all, an entire church-full of people had died, killed by Indians, a few miles from the spot where they now sat.

And they were sinners. Every one of them, including himself, Francis told them.

"But none of us need to continue in sin. Those of us who claim

Jesus as our Savior can walk each day, each moment in the power of God Almighty, being sanctified—that is, set apart from the ungodly."

Francis stepped down from the pulpit and walked among the congregation, fastening eyes with as many as would look at him. "Flee the evil desires of youth!" he said, eyeing a young man who probably used his handsome face, square jaw and flowing red hair to woo the girls of the village. "Destruction is its name. As King Solomon warned in Proverbs chapter seven: 'With persuasive words the seductress led the young man astray and he followed her like an ox going to the slaughter, like a deer stepping into a noose till an arrow pierces his liver, like a bird darting into a snare, little knowing it will cost him his life.'

"His life!" Francis added.

He stepped forward, down the aisle to his right. "Who among us can not set ourselves apart from the world by keeping a guard on our mouths? We can, if we but try, to stop lies, deceit, gossip, slander, blasphemy—all of them—from leaving our lips. Proverbs chapter eight teaches us 'You who are simple, gain prudence; you who are foolish, gain understanding. Listen, for I have worthy things to say. I open my lips to speak what is right, my mouth speaks what is true, for my lips detest wickedness. All the words of my mouth are just; none of them is crooked or perverse.'

"And, again in Second Timothy, Paul urges: 'Don't have anything to do with foolish and stupid arguments, because you know they produce quarrels. And the Lord's servant must not quarrel. Instead, he must be kind to everyone, able to teach, not resentful.'

"President Washington, when he was General Washington, had any man whipped who took the Lord's name in vain. Guess how many took the Lord's name in vain—"

"None?" little Thomas piped up from the Brackett family pew. Francis followed Thomas's voice, spotted him and smiled. "Very few, Thomas. Very few."

Francis turned and walked across the back of the room. Men were standing all along the back wall, eyes fastened on him.

People in the pews strained their necks to follow him.

"Who among us can not sprint away from those things that we know tempt us?" he resumed. "Lust! Lust of the flesh, lust for possessions, lust for power or control—even of a man's control over his wife. That lust for control, men, can be worse than the others."

"Amen!" The agreement came from the rear left corner of the room. Francis looked over and saw Harvey Smith standing. "Bishop! Dear Bishop!" Harvey said. "God Almighty has been convicting me since He showed me the way to the cross just yesterday. I didn't sleep all night because the conviction was so strong on my heart." Harvey looked down at his wife. "Forgive me, Grace."

Grace looked at her husband, lovingly, and a tear escaped down her cheek. "Of course, Harvey. Of course," she whispered hoarsely, putting her hand on his.

Applause greeted the exchange. Francis tried in vain to recall when he had ever heard applause in the midst of a sermon, but it didn't matter. Harvey had been delivered from the spirit of control.

Francis pointed to Harvey. "That's *sanctification*, dear ones. Harvey's being sanctified by the Holy Spirit working in his heart. He's being changed, his entire character, set apart by the Word of God and the Spirit of the Almighty. When Jesus prayed for His disciples in John chapter seventeen, he also prayed for us who would believe through their message. And when He did so, He said: 'I have given them the glory that You gave Me, that they may be one as we are one: I in them and You in Me.'

"The Holy Spirit is working in you, Harvey. Bless His name!"

Around the room, hands shot up toward the heavens. Harvey resumed his seat and Francis resumed his sermon as he walked back to the pulpit:

"First Thessalonians says: 'For this is the will of God, your sanctification: that you should abstain from sexual immorality; that each of you should know how to possess his own vessel in sanctification and honor, not in passion of lust, like the Gentiles who do not know God; that no one should take advantage of and defraud his brother in this matter, because the Lord is the avenger of all such, as we also forewarned you and testified. For God did not call us to uncleanness, but in holiness.'"

Stepping up to the pulpit, Francis looked over the room. The sun was peaking over the treetops now, shining through a small window behind him and causing what looked to some like a halo over him. "Now, may the good Lord bless and keep you. May He guard you in the fields and on the sea, may He steady your hand over the anvil, may He give strength in your chores, and may He bless your day—body, soul and spirit."

Reverend Matthews stood from the front row, faced the congregation and added, "And may He guide you back here this evening. Bishop Asbury will address us again at seven tonight. God be with you all."

•••••

When they returned to the Brackett home, Francis asked Abigail if he could help her in any of her chores. He'd done hard labor himself, he said, recalling his days as a youth when he apprenticed as a metalworker.

He and Nicholas spent the morning collecting hens' eggs and cleaning out a stall in the barn, where a mare had given off-season birth to a filly. The mare had at first considered their work an intrusion on her privacy, and rustled about trying to get comfortable as the filly nursed. But after a few minutes, she made leave of her baby and walked over to Francis. Perhaps she could sense that he loved horses. Perhaps Spark, in a stall at the other end of the barn, had shared stories with her, Francis thought with a smile.

He patted her nose, then nuzzled against her cheek. "You're a handsome lady. And, I'm betting, a good mother." She whinnied quietly, nodding her head as if she understood and agreed with the compliment.

"Her name's Ginger."

The voice was that of Abigail, who had entered through the large front doors. "My, you've done a masterful job here. Sam's coming in from the fields for lunch. Would you like to wash up and join us?"

Francis and Nicholas cranked up a bucket of water from a nearby well and washed their hands and faces. Refreshed, they joined their hosts at the dining table. Little Thomas was off at the village school. Sam blessed the food and Francis started the conversation.

"Horses," he said. "Ginger—there's a beauty."

"Yes, she is," Sam replied, "but it's our oxen we couldn't do without. Cattle can survive conditions that would kill Ginger. Not only are they our power for farming, but they also provide milk for us, manure for our fields, and, in the end, meat and leather."

"We couldn't farm without them," Sam said as he took a massive bite out of an egg-and-lettuce sandwich.

"Well, it's horses we couldn't do our work without," Nicholas said and laughed. "It's a long walk from any one place to another."

"We can travel in carriages over King's Path between New York City and Philadelphia," Francis said, "or the Boston Post Road between New York City and Boston, or the Common Road from Boston to Providence. But traveling from here to Maine is a bit more difficult. I'll bet it wasn't easy for you and Abigail—and all the others—to do what you must have done to settle here and make a home of it."

"Hard work and perseverance," Abigail replied.

"And horses," Sam added. "But while ours work the fields and carry produce to market, yours have traveled great distances, haven't they?"

Francis and Nicholas nodded.

"What's been your most difficult trek?" Abigail asked.

Nicholas looked questioningly at Francis, but it took no more than a second or two before Francis had the answer. "The Alleghenies," he said. "Crossing the Allegheny Mountains."

"Will you tell us about it?"

Francis nodded to his assistant. "Tell Sam and Abigail about the Alleghenies, Nicholas."

"They separate Pennsylvania and western Virginia from Virginia and Maryland. The problem is, that they rise thousands of feet toward the heavens. Stunning rock formations and groves of rhododendron abound. But as much as they are beautiful...."

"And windswept moors that remind me of the moors of England," Francis interjected.

"Bishop, you need to tell this story," Nicholas said.

"No, no, no. It's yours to tell, Nicholas."

With a shrug, Nicholas resumed. "Well, as beautiful as the Alleghenies are, they're dangerous. There's one highway, the Staunton-Parkersburg, that crosses over the mountains. The rest are animal and Indian trails, linking western Virginia and the Shenandoah Valley...."

"And it's over those Indian trails we've crossed dozens of times," Francis interjected again.

"Dear Bishop," Nicholas said, "please *do* tell the story. I've crossed over only twice with you, and I know you did it scores of times, and when it was a lot more dangerous than today."

"No, no, no, Nicholas. You tell the story," Francis insisted.

Nicholas looked warily at his mentor. "All right. Well, when the Iroquois and Cherokee tribes released their claims to the territory between the Ohio River and the Allegheny Mountains in 1768, people started moving west over the mountains. But when that happened, the Shawnee Indians began to attack them. And this began a dangerous *tete-a-tete* between colonists and Indians. In 1773 a number of colonists from Fort Fincastle in Wheeling murdered several Shawnee at Captina Creek."

"Yes, and about a year later," Francis cut in, "after two Shawnees committed a murder and robbery, a group of colonists, seeking revenge, murdered a canoe full of unarmed Mingo women and children and one man along the Kanawha River. It happened to be the entire family of Mingo Chief Tahgahjute, who was a long-time friend of the whites and who'd been baptized under the

English name of John Logan—the same name as William Penn's secretary. And although Logan had previously lived peacefully with colonists, he killed at least thirteen settlers, or even twice that many, that summer in revenge. He justified his actions as 'an eye for an eye.'

"A great and a sorrowful story, that," Francis said. "I knew Logan. A humble man. A quiet, peaceful man. No one could ever say he'd entered Logan's cabin hungry and Logan fed him not. Or that he ever came cold and naked and Logan clothed him not. During the entire bloody Revolution, Logan remained idle in his cabin, an advocate for peace. He was known far and wide for his love for the whites.

"But when Colonel Cresap murdered Logan's family in cold blood, leaving him with not one drop of his blood in the veins of any other living soul, he was filled with vile hatred. And he vented that hatred by murdering — murdering until it had fully glutted his vengeance."

"Revenge," said Sam. "It'll kill the killer as certainly as those he murders."

"And the Lord says, 'Vengeance is mine,'" Nicholas said.

"I wasn't there, but I can't help but think that Logan knelt at the cross and wept for forgiveness before his execution," Francis said. "And, I pray that, like the thief at Jesus' side, Logan met his Savior that day in Paradise."

All nodded at the thought of it.

•••••

"But, back to the Alleghenies," Sam urged.

Francis turned his hand toward Nicholas, deferring to his assistant.

"But I'm not a storyteller," Nicholas objected.

"Neither am I," Francis protested.

"But you truly are, Sir."

Francis turned to Sam. "Do you have a coin on you, Sam?"

With a puzzled look, Sam nodded, pulled one from his pocket

and handed it to him.

"Did you know that John and Charles Wesley, if they felt they weren't hearing from the Holy Spirit on a matter, would flip a coin?" Francis asked Sam.

"I'd heard that."

"It comes from the disciples drawing a straw when choosing a replacement for Judas."

"Tails, you tell the story, Nicholas. Heads, I do."

Francis flipped the coin, caught it and put it down in his palm.

When Francis revealed the coin, Nicholas smiled and folded his arms. "Heads. Ha! Tell on, Bishop."

Francis took a deep breath, ran a hand through his thick white hair and thought back to the day in Baltimore that he received a letter from Francis Poythress, whom he considered a brave hero of the faith. Poythress was one of Francis' itinerant preachers. He'd crossed the Alleghenies with pioneers and preached the gospel amidst plentiful perils.

"Dear Bishop, help!" Poythress wrote.

If he felt Francis should join him, then he would.

It proved not to be a hike for the weak of body or faint of heart. Indeed, nor if you feared the sight of death, this wasn't a trip you should take.

Speaking in a church in southwest Virginia, Francis said, "Jesus told His disciples to preach the Good News to the ends of the world. We stretched those ends when Columbus landed ashore at what is now Dominica. We stretched them farther with every boatload of British, French and Spanish Christians for the past two hundred years. *You* stretched it farther when your families ventured here to this valley.

"But is this the end of the world?"

Around the church, heads shook.

"No! Good Poythress has stretched the Good News over the Alleghenies and now calls for help. In three days' time, I'm leaving to traverse the Alleghenies and join him there to spread the gospel to the wilderness."

"Not alone, sir, surely." The booming voice was that of Carl Riley, who'd stood up in his pew and looked worriedly at Francis.

"Why, yes, Carl. That's my intention."

"But, Bishop, danger's at every hilltop," Carl protested. "Behind every tree, a savage could lay in wait!"

"The Lord will have His angels keep charge over me, Carl, as it says in Psalm ninety-one," Francis reassured him.

"Well, I'm volunteering to be the Lord's earthly watchman over you." Carl looked around the church. "Anyone else with me?"

"Aye, Carl," two or three men responded in unison.

"But who knows how long I'll be gone?" Francis protested.

Nevertheless, a dozen other voices joined in.

"I'll join."

"Sign me up."

"Me as well."

Carl smiled and looked at Francis. "Safety in numbers, Bishop—as well as in angels."

Three days later, Francis, Carl and about sixty others sat atop horses and wagons. Word had spread of the trip and several men and women longing for a new life with land of their own had decided to join them, bring along their families and meager possessions, and venture over the mountains.

Daniel Boone, taking his own family and five others with him, had started the migration route west over the Wilderness Road to Kentucky in 1773. George Rogers Clark, who traveled the same road, called Boone's Trace, had explored the interior in 1775.

Tales of Boone's excursions and settlements beyond the mountains had spread rapidly, kindling the urge in many to take advantage of the easy terms for acquiring land in Kentucky and Tennessee.

Four years before Francis' trip west, the Virginia Legislature had passed an act to provide for building a road to accommodate the people who were pioneering into Kentucky, but that hadn't happened yet. So this party of stalwarts faced traveling through the Cumberland Gap into northeast Tennessee and southeast Kentucky.

"Bishop! Bishop Asbury!"

Gripping the reins of his packhorse tightly, Francis turned in his saddle to see Billy Pickens run up to him. The rugged teenager sported a smile from ear to ear. "Bishop, we're coming, too! Dad and Mom and me! We're gonna start a new life. Find a meadow by a river, with rich soil. Fend for ourselves off the land and with God watchin' over our shoulders."

Francis could feel the boy's enthusiasm and he smiled to himself, thinking of his eagerness at that age for going out and preaching at places he'd never seen before.

"Wonderful, Billy." Francis looked beyond the boy to see if he could spot his parents and, sure enough, a ways back in the caravan Ted and Harriett Pickens sat in the seat on a wagon drawn by two horses, with all their worldly goods piled behind them.

"Uncle Andrew wrote us a letter urgin' us to come out to where he lives—on Roundstone River!"

Billy was exuberant. Francis winced. Did these people realize the difficulties ahead? Could these wagons even negotiate the mountain trails? He prayed for guidance, discernment, for God supernaturally to deliver them all to the other side of the rugged Alleghenies.

He was supposed to meet Poythress at Fort Boonesborough. But he was sure he'd travel all three territories by the time he was through. God willing.

•••••

Stunningly beautiful as the mountains were, they were, in some places, ferocious. They were meant to be crossed by sturdy stock. But the most important attribute of these pioneers, it became obvious early on, was determined faith, believing and knowing that a powerful God was ever-present to grant them strength, sustenance and endurance. How could non-believers survive in these wilds?

Little did he know in the crossing over that he would soon enough meet plenty of non-believers who had, indeed, passed over the Alleghenies and were, indeed, surviving in the wilderness. He wondered if that was maybe the grace of God, too.

Cumberland Gap was a pass in the Cumberland Mountains region of the Appalachians. Boone had hired thirty-five Transylvania Company axmen to widen an old Indian path into what people were calling the Wilderness Road. Felled trees lay this way and that alongside the "road," in some places exposing just how precarious the trip was. It was barely wide enough for the few wagons in his party to traverse safely; that would have to change soon, Francis thought. He looked up to the cliffs that overlooked the road both to the left and right and imagined Indians peering out from behind trees along the way.

Francis was preaching two times a day—morning and night— and sometimes at the noon hour if they could stop to eat. One of his most attentive listeners had become Billy Pickens. Billy had taken to walking alongside Francis and his packhorse, and sometimes hitching a ride by climbing up behind him when the going wasn't tough on Silver Fox. Inquisitive. Always inquisitive.

"What grand trees, Bishop!" he exclaimed once.

"There's lessons in these trees, Master Pickens."

"What be they, Sir?"

"Here's one." Francis pointed off to the side of the trail. "Do you see those fallen, decaying trees?"

Billy nodded.

"By the winnowing power of God, trees are here and there scattered on the forest floor. You can guess at how long ago they fell by the degree to which they've decayed.

"Eventually, the purpose of that deteriorating will be visible in the new, invigorated life of the vegetation around them. When a tree falls, it nourishes the next generation of trees. When we die, what we leave behind should also nourish those still alive, shouldn't it?"

Billy nodded assent.

"So, ask yourself: What have I done to nourish those who will be left behind?

"When Jesus died, Billy, He provided the greatest nourishment of all time. I just want to accomplish a small portion. How about you?"

Billy wandered off into deep thought, not answering the question.

The next day, Billy ran to the front of the wagon train and caught up to Francis.

"Young Master Pickens!" Francis acknowledged. "How do you fare this morning?"

"I've been thinking, Bishop. About what you said yesterday about the decaying trees. I, too, want to nourish others. What other lessons from the woods can you tell me?"

Carl, riding alongside Francis, chuckled at the youth's enthusiasm.

"Climb up here with me," Francis said, and leaned down to help pull Billy aboard Silver Fox. They were on fairly level ground for awhile and Silver Fox could stand the strain while Francis shared his story.

"Do you remember that big hawthorn tree next to your church back home?"

"Yessir."

"A healthy-looking specimen, right?"

"Right, sir."

"Bug-free?"

"Bug-free," Billy said with certainty.

"Well, Billy, before service on two successive days, I stood outside praying to God, and I noticed these two woodpeckers were pecking away at that hawthorn tree. I agree with you, that tree looked like the least likely candidate to serve up any treat of bugs for those woodpeckers. 'How could there be any bugs inside this healthy specimen?' I asked myself. There were certainly fewer healthy-looking trees immediately around it. Right?"

"Certainly, Bishop," Billy nodded with determination.

"Yet, these woodpeckers were coming to this one tree and apparently getting their daily fill. This is an object lesson, Billy."

"What's that, sir: an 'object lesson'?"

"Well, it means we can learn something from it. Think of that tree as a person. A man or woman may *look* free of spiritual 'bugs.' They may fool the world about how 'healthy' they are spiritually. But if there's anything amiss inside them—any pest eating away at their soul—it will be found out. And when it is, the process of extricating it from within them is bound to be painful.

"Psalm forty-four, verse twenty-one says: 'Would God not have discovered it, since He knows the secrets of the heart?'

"And Psalm ninety, verse eight declares that God has set our iniquities before Him, our secret sins in the light of His presence."

"Ain't no hidin', then," Billy said.

"No hiding, Billy. May the Lord grant us discernment, both to look inward within ourselves and inward within others. And may He grant us courage to stand in the faith firmly against that which would destroy our souls, and to help deliver others who are being beset by the enemy."

"The enemy being Satan?" Billy asked.

"The enemy being Satan."

They were approaching another difficult hill, so Francis turned in his saddle and faced Billy. "Better get down now, son. Listen to God and He Himself will teach you lessons in the things around you."

Billy slid off Silver Fox and looked up. "But will you teach me some more later, too?"

Francis nodded, and the teaching did continue.

But the farther they got along the trail, the more Francis prayed—eight, ten, twelve times a day. The Treaty of Sycamore Shoals, signed in 1775, had ended most Indian troubles. But the operative word was "most."

•••••

Francis, Carl and the others in the journey soon saw first-hand that survival and luxury were two distinct things. A week into their journey—fighting off gnats, fixing broken wagon wheels, and pushing and pulling stuck wagons out of deep ruts in the trail— they came upon three log cabins, nearby one another. Raccoon and wildcat skins hung round the walls. Deer horns were strewn over the roof of one cabin. Wild turkeys' wings stuck out from the cracks of another.

Adornments, Francis thought. *These pioneers' versions of pillars beautifying their homes.*

Suddenly, the tallest man Francis had ever seen stepped out from behind the middle cabin. A fistful of beet greens filled one hand and a Kentucky long rifle the other.

Francis was reminded of how the Israelites rebuilt the walls of Jerusalem under Ezra and Nehemiah – working with one hand while holding weapons of defense with the other. Here, in this wilderness, one went about life cautiously and precariously.

"Yo!" the man called out. "Looks like guests!"

Francis looked around to see if the man was speaking to a comrade or wife, or to himself. No one else appeared to be about. He smiled at the thought of this mountain man hosting a party of fifty. He appeared not to have bathed in an eon. His full beard hadn't seen a scissor or razor in just as long. A broad-brimmed hat made of some sort of hide covered his head; another type of skin had been fashioned into britches and he wore what appeared to be a store-bought shirt with a string to tie up a V-neck. He hadn't tied it.

One of God's children, Francis thought. "Sir," Francis said, "would you mind if we stopped and rested here in this field for the night?"

"Well, course not! Welcome, welcome!" Setting down his beet greens, the man stepped forward and extended his hand. "John Wheeler," he said. "Call me 'Shank.'"

Francis reached down to shake his hand. "Shank?"

"Ate the entire shank of a cow once. Someone called me Shank. It stuck."

Francis looked up and down this six-foot-six-or-so giant standing before him and nodded. "Shank it is. I'm Francis Asbury, this is Carl Riley and our little band of travelers is heading to the other side of the Alleghenies."

Suddenly, doors opened from both of the other cabins and women stuck their heads out. The wailing of a baby came from the farthest cabin, while several children apparently were playing about in the other, behind their mother.

Seeing the caravan of travelers, the first woman stepped outside her cabin and waved a welcome. The other woman, an apron tied around her waist and a kerchief over her head, also stepped outside and turned to her very tall neighbor. "Shank, check out that deer Herbert brought home t'other day and see if you think it mightn't feed this lot, will ya?"

"It was a big buck. Dressed out to over a hundred pounds, Martha. I'm sure it will."

"Then blow on that ram's horn o' yorn and get our men-folk home so's we can welcome these people proper."

"Yes, ma'am." Shank pulled a double-twisted horn from the belt tied around his waist and blew mightily on it. An ear-splitting shrill echoed through the surrounding hills. Shank looked at Francis and, beneath his broad hat, an eyebrow raised in humor. "Our call home."

Francis climbed down from Silver Fox and tethered his packhorse to a tree.

The two pioneer women introduced themselves as Martha Stedman and Mary Andrews and immediately walked toward the travelers, who were circling their wagons around a field opposite the cabins. "We'll provide the meat for a wholesale cookout," Martha said. "Do you folks have rice, or taters, or veggies t' share?"

"It's just like a church supper," said Elizabeth Perkins, who sat atop one of the wagons. "Only outdoors! Sure we've got vegetables, potatoes—!"

Francis watched in amazement as the women of the caravan climbed down from their wagons and hurried to work together to prepare a feast. *The Lord must have put this desire within women,* he thought, *to be nurturers and care-givers. Just look at them!*

The men? Well, they could hunt, they could build, they could farm, but that sense of feeding and caring for others wasn't their strongest point. He thought of his mother. She'd be in her element here, gathering people to feed them and share the gospel. Bold and confident, she'd show the love of Christ to every woman, man and child here, treating them all, saved or unsaved, alike. He whimsically felt homesick, then slapped himself back to reality. A grown man—homesick for his mother!

Shank sidled up to Francis. "Mister Asbury, would you and some t'others like to sleep inside my cabin tonight?" He opened the door to Francis and Carl. Even though there was daylight left outside, it was dark inside and Shank hurried to light a candle on an old, hand-made table in the center of the room.

Francis looked around. A dirt floor. A sour smell mixed with, what, mildew? Sparse and simple furniture. A small fireplace, with a pot hanging at its center. Francis felt a tickle on his ankle, then the other ankle. Fleas!

"Nice. Nice," Francis said to Shank. "But tonight I prefer sleeping under the stars since it's not raining. And I expect we'll see the Milky Way tonight."

Carl backed toward the door. "Me, too, Shank, and I think most of the others. But I'll ask around. Thanks for the offer. You've built a, er, fine home here."

"Needs a woman's touch, though," Shank declared.

"A woman's fine touch makes a house a home," Francis said. "Like the Master's touch on us transforms our stone-cold hearts to warm hearts."

"Sounds like a preacher preachin'," Shank declared.

"'Tis," Francis replied.

Shank broke out in a smile so loud it almost cried out.

"Then preach t'us t'night, preacher! We'll have at least three cabins worth of eight people and I'll round up some others 'round about."

"Count it done!" Francis shook the man's hand and the deal was complete. He'd have his first pioneer audience that night!

Several hours later, the weary caravan of travelers sat around small fires in the field. Every few minutes a pioneer, or a family of pioneers, would walk up the path and join the crowd. Raggedly clothed, often unwashed, these people welcomed the travelers like long-lost family. Love simply poured out of them. And yet Francis knew many, if not most, didn't know the Lord. His heart swelled with the thought of saved souls.

Dear Lord, give me the words to preach in Your power. Deliver these souls into Your pasture, he prayed.

When everyone was finally sitting on the ground or on logs in a circle in the field, Shank stepped into the center. His voice boomed. "Neighbors, we're privileged to have a preacher here who's traveled the colonies. He weren't born here; he was born in England; but we forgive him that."

Laughter erupted.

"Show Mister Asbury the respect he's owed. This ain't entertainment. Tis serious." Shank glared hard at one older man leaning against a tree and holding an old English Brown Bess against his shoulder. "Cal? Behave."

Shank searched the faces around him and stopped at one—a gruff-looking, bearded fellow wearing a coonskin hat and with a long musket strapped over his shoulder. "You, too, Howard. Tis my home, or close to it, and I expect reverence for the Book. Whether you believe it or you don't."

Howard growled but nodded, then turned to the woods beside him and said, "I'll be watchin' for Injuns."

Howard also held a tomahawk, reminding Francis that the small axe was often the weapon of choice for settlers who found gunpowder too expensive to use all the time.

"Good." Shank turned to Francis, put a hand to his hat and said, "Mister Asbury, our ears are yourn, sir."

Francis opened his Bible to Proverbs and read from chapter eleven, verse three: "The integrity of the upright guides them, but the duplicity of the treacherous destroys them."

He looked around the field and at the pioneer women seated outside their cabins. Martha's husband stood behind her and she held his hand next to her head. Mary was cradling her baby, her little finger in his mouth.

"Walking through these woods," Francis said, "I find there's a wealth of knowledge you can learn from God's creation. All about us are lessons to be learned. Here's one.

"It's often easy to identify how the health of some trees is affected by their environment, or the trees surrounding them. There may be two trees of equal age and type, yet one overshadows the other. Just look at this large oak and the little one next to it. Once in the shade of the larger tree, the smaller one will fall further and further behind in height and girth because it needs the sun in order to flourish.

"It's important for people to begin their journey with God at an early age so that they'll not be affected by others who'll not help them to grow, but rather to wither."

Francis winked at Billy Pickens, then noticed Cal shake his head disapprovingly and look away out into the woods.

"The stories are legend about the power of 'peer pressure,'" Francis continued. "But that message is normally a negative one, warning you to not be affected by peer pressure! To watch out for peer pressure; it will pull you into sin!

"But I declare to you today: Why not view it the other way around? I say, *be* the peer pressure! Don't be overshadowed by sinners, but, like that big oak over there, be the shade for them.

"If we walk in the light, exuding life, vibrancy and love, then others around us will see that zest and want it for themselves. They'll ask, 'What is the source of your joy and integrity?' And you'll stand tall with the answer that will give them life!"

Francis turned to some in his traveling party. "Do you understand? Jesus Himself wasn't affected by peer *pressure*. If He had been, He never would have declared to the world who He was. No! Jesus *became* the peer pressure. He walked the world *as* the peer pressure. Now it's up to you who are His disciples to *be* the peer pressure. Wherever you travel, wherever you settle, Jesus wants you to **be** the peer pressure, firmly grounded in the Word and shining the light of His glory."

Francis saw Shank raise a hand. "Yes, Shank?"

"Well, Mister Asbury, we're pretty busy just stayin' alive out here. Slavin' all day, growin' food or huntin' it. Not much time left for preachin' the gospel."

"Shank, you don't have to preach. The most important thing any of us can do is to simply *be*. You're a human being, not a human doing. If you be God's son, people will see Him through you. But 'being' means 'showing.' In your living and working and hunting and growing food, in watching over your family and neighbors, in repairing your traps and cleaning your rifles —," he glanced at Howard, "or sharpening your tomahawk. In all of these things you can allow the fruit of the Holy Ghost to be apparent through you."

"Fruit of the Holy Ghost?"

"Love, joy, peace, patience, kindness, goodness, faithfulness, gentleness and self-control."

"Ha! Self-control! Got a problem with that, hey, Shank?" Cal apparently hadn't lost interest, after all.

Shank scowled at Cal. "You sayin' you don't?"

"I ain't sayin' I don't. But I ain't sayin' I'm no Christian, neither. So's I don't have to show no self-control." Cal laughed.

"No, and you won't have no love 'n joy 'n peace and all that other stuff, neither," Shank retorted.

"Well, that ain't no bizness o' yourn, is it?" Cal took a step away from the tree and toward Shank, who stood a good twenty yards away.

Francis sized up Cal. He compared to Shank as a rat to a cat. *An unfortunate comparison*, he thought to himself, imagining the quick work any scuffle between these two would be. *Is this Cal fellow crazy?*

Francis stepped in front of Cal and looked him straight in the eye.

"Are you a gambler, Cal?"

"Gambler?"

"Well, it appears to me that indeed you *are* a gambler, facing off with a man of Shank's, ah-h, Shank's stature."

Cal stopped in his tracks and Francis pressed on. "Do you

know that in the world of gambling the house always wins?"

"Ah-h. Guess so." Even though aggravated with Francis stepping in front of him, Cal was obviously curious as to where this train of thought was going.

"Listen, I understand, Cal. You live in a world of gambles. Gambles there'll be venison on the table tomorrow, that no bear'll tear up your garden, that the hens'll keep laying eggs for another month. Living in this wilderness, you gamble that those Indians Henry's looking out for over there aren't on a warpath this very night."

"Then everyone here's a gambler." Cal folded his arms, deflecting what he thought to be a personal affront. "And who's 'the house'?"

Francis looked about them. "That's a good question, Cal. Who's 'the house'? What 'house' do you think it is that would want you to go on living without going to Someone greater than you for protection? What 'house' would hope you continue living without love, peace, joy and, as Shank said, 'all that other stuff'? And, finally, what 'house' would have you hold off on repentance?"

Cal looked quizzically at Francis.

"The answer, Cal, is 'Satan's house'!" Francis slowly turned around in a circle and addressed everyone. "Listen, I may never pass this way again, friends. You may say, 'That's all right. I can come to God any time. Doesn't matter if this Asbury fellow is here or not.'

"Yes, it's true that Scripture says Christ stands at the door always, waiting for you to open it to Him. But will you be alive to open it? You're gambling with every day, every hour, every minute you don't make Christ the Lord of your life. Will you repent now? There may never be a tomorrow for you."

Francis looked squarely at Cal. "If you stand still this moment, casting this opportunity aside—or thinking tomorrow will be a bright day for salvation—then you **are** a gambler, and you're on the wrong side of the bet, my friend. Those Indians might indeed be on a warpath tonight. You might fall off a cliff on your way home."

Again, he turned around. "Choose now, friends. Choose now, or gamble on the eternal state of your very souls! It's a hot hell, with fires constantly stoked, that awaits you at one place.

"It's a glorious heaven, with hallelujahs ringing through God's throne room, that awaits you at the other. Hades or jubilee?

"Choose now!"

•••••

Francis beamed at the memory of that night. It became a long one. People didn't want to return to their homes. Having eaten the meat in their meal, they wanted to hear more meat from the Word of God.

The next morning, as everyone was preparing to leave, Shank approached Francis. "Mister Asbury, thank you from the bottom of my heart. Your preachin' changed me."

He offered his hand and Francis shook it. "You're welcome, Shank. God is good, if men will only seek Him."

"I wanted to ask you about Cal and Howard."

"Yes."

"I can't say that I like either one of them men, but the good Lord says I'm supposed to. How do I do that, seein' that Howard's a puddin' head and Cal's thick as two short planks?"

Francis sized up his new friend, this grizzly-looking giant with a soft heart.

"First, resist thinking of them as a puddin' head or thick as two short planks," Francis said, smiling. "Listen, Shank, Matthew chapter twenty, verse twenty-eight tells us, that Jesus came not to be ministered unto, but to minister. Here's what you do: Love the unsaved and serve the unsaved not because you love them but because God does, and not as a service to that person but as a service to God.

"John Wesley wrote a creed that I go by: 'Do all the good you can, by all the means you can, in all the ways you can, in all the places you can, at all the times you can, to all the people you can, as long as you ever can.'"

"That's a whole load of doin'." Shank shook his head in doubt.

"And I'd add 'in every house, tavern, kitchen and shop.' Remember, you can do all things through Christ Who strengthens you. Just call on Him for that strength, Shank. I trust you'll get it."

Shank bear-hugged him until Francis gasped for air and begged his leave. He felt like a mouse in the grip of an eagle.

CHAPTER 9

Attacked by Indians

Two mornings after leaving Shank and Mary and Martha's families, Francis and his fellow travelers were on the path heading west. They were always on their guard. Besides Carl, several other men had come on the trip to ensure protection for Francis. Douglas Bane, Zedekiah Clift, William Breckenridge and Levi Barnette rode horses or walked behind the wagon train. Martin Poag, Jackson Klaiber and Arthur Dixon rode behind Francis and in front of the lead wagon.

Francis had taken to tying his packhorse to the back of the first wagon. With Billy walking by his side, he was in the midst of another lesson from the nature around them. "Notice the birds, Billy. They're creatures of habit, mining their morning ration of bugs or worms. You can count on it, every day. They have a pattern of behavior. They're creatures of habit, and God wants us to be *preachers* of habit, going about sharing His Word.

"Timothy was a young man who helped the apostle Paul. Lately, when I read about him I think of you – thirsty for the truth. Paul wrote to Timothy: 'Preach the Word. Be prepared in season and out of season. Correct, rebuke and encourage—with great patience and careful instruction.'"

Francis looked down at Billy to see if he was showing interest, and found a face in rapt attention.

"One of my words to live by is from Puritan Pastor Richard Baxter. He said, 'I preach as never to preach again, and as a dying man to dying men.'"

Billy looked astonished and anxious. "Do you think you're going to die, Bishop?"

Francis laughed. "I think I'll die when I've finished the job God's given me, Billy. And I don't believe I have. Not by a long while."

Billy smiled.

Just then, Carl, who rode in front of Francis, called out, "Trouble ahead!" Carl looked back behind him and pointed in that direction. Smoke swirled above the trees, straight west as the crow flies from their position.

Francis leaned forward in his saddle and asked, "Could that be Fort Harrod?"

"Naw, we've not traveled that far."

Rodney Yates, a blacksmith by trade, rode up beside Francis, listening in, and added: "And Fort Boonesborough's further than that."

"It could be a coupla cabins of settlers," Carl said. "A lot of these settlers clear their land and build their cabins during the day, but return to sleep in the safety of the fort at night. Safe for them but not for their cabins, I'm afraid."

"Well," Rodney said, "maybe it's a forest fire. Too big for a campfire, for sure."

"Billy, you'd better get back with your family," Francis said. Billy nodded and ran back toward the Pickens' wagon.

A slow drizzle began. Francis, Carl and Rodney started to quicken their horses' pace toward the smoke, but Martin Poage reached forward and tugged at Francis. "Bishop, you should stay behind. Jackson and Arthur can watch over you while I go ahead with Carl and Roddy."

Francis shook his head. "You come, too, Martin, but I must go—in case someone needs spiritual help."

"If you insist, sir."

"I do."

Martin turned to Jackson Klaiber and Arthur Dixon. "Why don't you stay back here with the wagons, and I'll go ahead with the bishop and t'others? Arthur, you tell the fellas at the back of the wagon train, okay?"

Jackson and Arthur nodded agreement, pulling their long rifles from their saddles, and Arthur rode off to the rear.

As Francis and the others rode on, they came upon a pasture. Carl turned to Martin. "Here's a good spot to circle the wagons. Go tell everyone to come on ahead but only to this field." Martin turned back and rode back along the caravan to tell everyone the plan.

Carl, Rodney and Francis rode only a few hundred yards before they came upon the source of the smoke: four cabins, each within sight of the other, obviously built close together for mutual protection.

"Phew!" Carl responded. "The stink of destruction."

"The stink of death," Rodney replied.

Francis dismounted Silver Fox and slowly walked around the smoldering ruins of the first cabin. He pulled his coat tight about him and turned up his collar, for the rain was bringing a cold snap with it. What he saw was saddening. Only one wall stood, centered by a stone fireplace. All else was charred ruin. The stick of a table leg wabbled eerily in the center of the rubble. As Francis leaned his head to look closer, he noticed why it was standing. It was in the grasp of a hand. Blackened, its skin peeled by the heat, a corpse lay flat out on what had been the floor.

Asbury stepped into the debris and approached the charred body. It was a woman, perhaps in her thirties. A wedding band hung loosely on her right ring finger, so she was European, Francis thought. *Come all this way for a new life and what did you find, my dear?* He wondered. *I pray you found the new life of an eternal kind before this horror befell you.*

"Let's check the other cabins to see if there's anyone left alive," Carl said. "Then we'd better get our people moving to try to find a safe place for the night."

Francis made his way back to Silver Fox, took her reins and walked to the next cabin and the next and the next after that. Death and destruction were everywhere! And far worse than the first cabin. Three children and two parents were all dead in one. Two men and two teenage boys in another. A baby with its mother and father, along with two older children, in another. Twenty-four dead in all. Twenty-four!

Francis fell to his knees and heaved tears of sorrow. Twenty-four souls! Were they reached with the gospel? Had one single preacher traveled this far, struggled this far, persevered this far to reach them? Were these some of the pioneers to whom Poythress had shared the salvation message? Francis could only hope so, for, if not, it was certainly too late for their souls now.

The burnt remnants of lives was sickening. And it was terrifying. A shiver went down Francis' spine. Then, kneeling on the ground, he realized the author of terror of the horror around him wasn't man, but Satan. Their battle was not just against these Indians, but the spirit that controlled them, that drove them to hatred and murder.

Francis was suddenly struck by the awful and awesome challenge for God's preachers. You could never rest in any knowledge that there would be enough time to save all who could be saved in the time you had on this earth.

Francis recalled the quote he had shared with Billy, "I preach as never to preach again and as a dying man to dying men." He himself was certainly too late to do these poor folks any good. He took a handkerchief from his pocket and wiped his face dry, but the cries still penetrated his soul with grief. The pain! The anguish! The hot depths of eternal hell to where the unsaved had perished—and to where these savages would die as well!

Francis looked up to the heavens, and as raindrops began to fall on his face, he called out, "Quicken my pace, Lord! Quicken us all who carry Your Word!"

At that moment he determined that these pioneers would not go without the Word of God. He would see to that. Carl sent Rodney back to see to it that after the wagons were in a circle, a contingent of men came with shovels to bury the dead.

That night the caravan pulled tightly together and Carl separated the men into four night watches. "Stay alert or we may all die!" he said as he gathered them around. Of the fifty people, Asbury counted about twenty-five who had arms. That meant six per watch.

Helen Ames, a middle-aged woman with three toddlers draped about her legs, approached Francis. "I'm afraid, Mister Asbury." Indeed, she shivered in fright.

"Fear comes with this territory, I'm afraid," he said.

"But do we have enough armed men to protect us?"

"Dear lady," Francis said, "do you believe the six sentries for each watch are our only protection?"

Helen looked bewildered.

"Remember Psalm ninety-one. 'He will give His angels charge to keep watch over thee, to keep thee in all of thy ways. They will hold you in the palm of their hands so you will not strike your foot upon a stone.' Yes, we have only six men per watch. But, no—and absolutely no—they are not our only protection. In fact, they are not even our best protection by a very long distance.

"Angels, dear one, defeated mighty armies of thousands and tens of thousands for the children of Israel. And are you not a child of Israel, grafted into the tree by your faith in Christ?"

Helen nodded.

"Then fear not. God's Word tells us that fear is a sin. It shows absence of faith. And what can worry add to your life, eh? White hairs maybe, but that's all. And you're much too young to be sprouting white hairs!"

Helen smiled. "Thank you, pastor."

"Thank God," he replied and hugged her warmly.

Nevertheless, as the people slept restlessly that night, and the next and the next as they moved on, Francis awakened during all four watches to make his way from one sentry to the next, praying without ceasing for the safety of these brave people.

•••••

Then one mid-morning, Francis and Carl, traveling side by side at the front of the caravan, spotted the Laurel River only a hundred yards ahead of them. Just then, Douglas Bane, who had watch at the rear of the caravan, rode at a fast pace to the front.

"Indians!" Douglas called, gasping for breath and pulling his horse to a halt.

"Where?" asked Carl. Alarm rang in his question and twisted his face.

"Trailing us, about a half-mile back." Douglas waved broadly behind him. "I spotted 'em from the hilltop back there."

Carl waved to Zedekiah, William and Levi. "Ride on back with Douglas and tell everyone to drive with haste," Carl said. "We're close to the river crossing and we'll have to get over before the Indians attack."

Douglas and the other three men turned their horses and rode back, repeatedly calling out, "Speed it up! Speed it up to the river ahead! Indians are trailing us!"

Francis also turned Silver Fox and followed after them.

"Mister Asbury, where are *you* going?" Carl called after him.

Francis whistled into Silver Fox's ear to hurry him on, and hollered back, "To be with the men at the rear."

"But you're not armed!"

"Oh, yes I am!" Francis replied. And off he went.

Carl shook his head in resignation.

"OK, Elijah," he said to Elijah White, whose wagon was in the lead this day. "Spur them on to the river. Follow me. I know the crossing point in the river flow."

Elijah turned to his wife beside him and children in the wagon. "Hold on, Mildred; children!"

The path was bumpy, with tree roots sticking out of the ground here and there, and it was a rough-and-tumble ride. Every single person in every wagon feared a wheel would fall off, or they would be tossed overboard by the bumps.

"Pray, people. Pray!" Francis called as he rode along, passing the wagons of the Aldersons and the Belchers, the Baileys and the Cloyds, the Clays and the Ingles. "Remember King David as he went into battle! Call on the mighty right hand of God!"

The response was immediate from many of the people. In

wagon after wagon, children screamed as they were bounced about. Their mothers cautiously climbed into the wagon beds with them.

Geoffrey Alderson hollered as he extended a whip to his horses' backs. "We're in your hands, Lord!"

Mitchell Belcher cried out, "Speed us onward, Father. Keep the wheels tight!"

Francis, close on the heels of the other men, reached the rear wagon, where Martin Poage, Jackson Klaiber and Arthur Dixon all sat atop their horses, intently looking down the gradual slope of the trail behind them. Douglas pointed to their rear and told of the Indians he had seen.

"A raiding party, I'm sure of it," he said. "Perhaps twenty of 'em."

When he spoke, the men readied their long rifles, loading them with musket-shot.

As they did so, Francis quoted from Psalm 18: "As for God, His way is perfect, the Word of the Lord is flawless. He is a shield for all who take refuge in Him. For Who is God besides the Lord? And Who is the Rock except our God? It's God Who arms me with strength and makes my way perfect. He makes my feet like the feet of a deer; He enables me to stand on the heights. He trains my hands for battle; my arms can bend a bow of bronze. You give me your shield of victory and your right hand sustains me; You stoop down to make me great. You broaden the path beneath me, so that my ankles do not turn."

"We need to fend off the Indians and at the same time not lose sight of our wagons," Douglas said. "Who's got the longest rifles here?"

He looked around. Longer barrels meant increased accuracy for long-range shots. Such guns needed more powder and used smaller balls, but the higher muzzle velocity gave them a flatter trajectory and thus better accuracy at a longer range.

"Zedekiah, William, Levi," you three take the first shots when they get within range. When you reload, Martin, Jackson and I will fire, and while we're reloading," he looked around and noticed that Ted Ingles and Jacob Clay had joined them. "Ted, Jacob and Arthur will shoot. Then we'll all retreat to the rear wagon and do it all over again."

Douglas looked at Francis. "Mister Asbury?"

"Yes, Douglas?"

"Keep praying, will ya? Loud, so's we can hear?"

"Yes, sir."

Levi Barnette, in a hoarse whisper, declared, "I see 'em. Down there, through the pines."

"All right, men, wait for a good shot before you start firing. And if you see that they know we've spotted 'em, start firing anyway."

The men all nodded consent.

"Now's the time," Zedekiah said. William and Levi, just as alert, took aim. "Now!" Zedekiah said, and the three men fired their long rifles. Francis looked down the hill toward the Indians and noticed one of the two in the lead recoil and grip his stomach. Another bullet smacked off a tree beside another of the two Indians in the lead.

Douglas said, "OK, men, move behind us and we'll take our shots."

As Zedekiah, William and Levi squatted to the side and moved behind, Douglas, Martin and Jackson stood side by side and took aim. The Indian in the lead and several others began to urge on their horses. "Take your shots when you can get 'em, men," Douglas said.

Bam. Bam. Bam. One by one they discharged their loads.

Praying aloud, Francis noticed another Indian get hit—this time on a shoulder, and spin off his horse, falling to the ground. A second horse reared up, apparently hit by another bullet, and its rider struggled to keep it under control.

Rather than hide behind trees, the rest of the Indian hunting party set their horses into a full gallop up the hill toward them.

Douglas, Martin and Jackson stepped out of the way and Arthur, Ted and Jacob took their places, aiming at the Indians who were now within a couple hundred yards.

Bam. Bam. Bam.

"Retreat, men! Retreat to the rear wagon!" Douglas called.

As all the men swept their long rifles onto their shoulders and ran to their horses, Francis took another look down the hillside. The Indians were gaining ground quickly. Holding their horses' manes with one hand and holding bows in the other.

"Slow them down, Lord! Make them stumble!" he cried out. He turned Silver Fox to race back to the wagons and prayed to God for a hedge of protection on the men. Over tree roots and the rough trail the ten men raced.

The sounds of fear were all about Francis.

"Yah!" hollered Zedekiah.

"Git up!" screamed Levi.

"Watch out!" William howled at Jackson as Jackson nearly knocked him into a tree.

"Hurry up! Hurry up!" Douglas called to the caravan up ahead. Those who were driving the wagons were obviously hustling as quickly as they could over the rugged terrain, but everyone knew that the Indians were to them like a rabbit to a turtle.

At the front of the caravan, Carl had reached the Laurel River and found the passage point. "As fast as you can, Elijah!" he shouted and waved him into the waters. The river was flowing at a steady but not rapid pace, thankfully. And it was fairly flat at the point where the wagons were to enter the flow.

Elijah White urged his two horses into the river with a loud cry. After one step of trepidation, both horses sprang forward, tugging the wagon behind them. The water was two to three feet deep.

"Keep on going when you get to the other side," Carl called. "We need to make sure there's room enough for all the wagons to cross over. And, Elijah?"

"Yeah?" Elijah hollered back to Carl, who had disappeared from his sight behind him.

"When you pull up, get back to the river with your long rifle. I think we'll need ya here."

"Gotcha!"

By this time, the second wagon was at the river, its horses

stepping into the waters. Ted Pickens was at the reins, his wife Harriet beside him and Billy in the wagon.

"Fast as you can!" Carl urged.

•••••

Francis and the riflemen had just caught up to the rear-most wagon, and the men all slid off their horses and tied them to tree branches at the side of the trail. They hid behind trees and bushes, and Douglas said, "Same order of fire, men."

Just then, the first Indians crested the hill about a hundred yards behind them. *They've narrowed the distance by half*, Francis guessed from his seat atop Silver Fox. He quickly maneuvered the horse behind a large evergreen, giving himself just enough room to peer around it to the trail behind them.

"Lord," he said, "it doesn't appear You held them back one step! Now, I know You tell us to concentrate on things that are pure and lovely and of good report, but that's difficult to do at this very moment!"

Silver Fox was unsteady underneath him, whinnying and anxiously moving her hind legs to the left and right. Francis patted her neck reassuringly. "Steady, girl. Steady."

Then he continued, "Please, Father, please protect our men and women and children. Confuse these Indians as you did the Chaldeans who attacked the Hebrews! And, somehow, Lord, use this to bring them to salvation."

"Shoot when you're ready," Douglas said to Zedekiah, William and Levi. A few seconds later, bam. Bam. Bam.

Another ball of lead found its mark in the neck of one of the Indians, while a second struck an Indian in a hand and the third missed altogether. Again, Douglas, Martin and Jackson took aim. But, by then, the other Indians in the war party apparently dismounted their horses.

Apparently. As Francis prayed from behind the big tree, he noticed movement through its branches to his left. Squinting to see what it was, he noticed two more Indians on horseback, weaving their way between trees, gliding along as smoothly as a snake between rocks.

"Ted—Jacob," Francis called hoarsely to the two men nearest him. "Over there!"

He pointed in the direction of the Indians who were trying to get around behind them.

"What?" Ted asked.

"Indians! Two of them on horseback."

"I see 'em," Jacob said and pointed. "Hey, Arthur, over here."

Ted, Jacob and Arthur all moved into position to get shots.

Hearing the commotion, Douglas called back, "What's happenin'?"

"Indians—flanking around us," Francis replied, pointing.

"What about the other side?" Douglas asked, nodding to Francis' right.

"I don't know." Francis scanned that direction for any signs of movement. Two more!

"Yes! Yes! Right there!"

Directly to his right, about seventy-five yards distant, two other Indians were also trying to outflank them. These two, however, were having a more difficult time of it because the woods were thick there, not allowing easy passage.

Douglas raised his rifle, took aim and—too quickly Francis thought—fired. Smack! The slug caromed off a hardwood tree and struck one of the Indians in the shoulder, knocking him from his horse. The Indian riding with him yelped in fury, pulled his horse to a halt, then looked in their direction. He locked eyes with Francis and Francis felt he could read the soul of the man. A savage filled with hatred? Apparently so, but why? The question would continue to vex and haunt him for years.

At that moment, an arrow, two, three—a dozen!—filled the air in downward projectiles.

"Take cover!" Douglas screamed as one arrow hit the ground not a foot away.

Ted and Jacob were taking aim at the two Indians skirting

around them. The trees made it difficult to get a clear target.

"Can't do it," Ted declared.

"Then we'll have to get back and get them before they reach the wagons," Jacob declared.

"Get back! Get back!" Douglas ordered.

The men all ran to their horses, hopped on their saddles and turned again toward the rear of the wagon train.

•••••

At the river's edge, Carl hollered non-stop to those driving the wagons. "Hurry! Hurry! But don't let the horses spook!"

All the time, he was praying that none of the wagons would lose a wheel. That would doom them all because the passage point was so narrow. Twelve of the sixteen wagons had crossed over and eight of the men aboard them who had firearms had returned to the riverbank on the other side, readying to fire at the first sight of an Indian.

"Keep a sharp eye, but don't fire before you have a clean shot!" Rodney Yates warned. The blacksmith held a Kentucky long rifle in a grip that threatened to leave a permanent imprint.

"When was the last time you fired that thing, Roddy," asked Ken Ames beside him.

"Don't recall." Rodney fixed him with an unflinching eye. "But pity the fool that tries to harm my own."

"I believe it!" Ken said, a smile playing at the corners of his mouth as he eyed the broad shoulders and muscles hardened by years at an anvil. "Glad I'm on your side, my friend."

Rodney simply nodded, then returned his gaze to the woods on the other side of the river. "Where are they?"

"Here they come," called Mitchell Belcher, one of the men on the riverbank. He nervously fingered the trigger of his long rifle. Around a bend in the trail came nine men on horseback. Levi Barnette's hat flew off his head, but he wasn't about to stop or go back for it. Long rifles banged on the backs of the men—all except that of Francis—and Mitchell thought what a sight Francis made on that big white steed of his, just like, he imagined, George Washington leading his troops.

Francis didn't feel like George Washington leading an army against the tyrants of England. He felt like a prayer warrior concerned for his "army."

As the other men with him again dismounted to take positions, Francis carried on, riding to the river. Zachary Cloyd was at the reins of the last wagon and there was one ahead of him, just entering the river and driven by Herbert Bailey.

Just then, Bailey's wagon began to falter and tip.

"Watch out there!" Francis called.

Herbert turned to his children in the wagon and pointed at a barrel on the right side. "Throw that barrel overboard!"

Three youngsters, none older than ten, all shaking in fear, obeyed their father while their mother scurried from the front seat to help them. "One, two, three!" she counted and, with a mighty heave, the barrel rose and slipped over the sideboard and into the river.

Just as suddenly as it had tipped, the wagon righted itself. The children stood up and yelled, "Hooray!" Herbert drew a deep breath and snapped his whip over the heads of his two horses. They lurched ahead and one of the boys fell overboard to the downstream side.

He hit the water, came back up and flailed away, screaming, "Mommy! Daddy! Help! Help!" His head went under the water and bobbed back up again, his arms swinging like a windmill, his mouth gasping for air.

Francis urged Silver Fox into the river and rode toward the boy. He had fallen far enough off the sand-bar that the water was slightly over his head—perhaps three-and-a-half feet deep—and carrying him away.

He submerged, then emerged again. This time, as he raised his arm in the air, Francis tightened his thighs and gripped Silver Fox's mane for leverage with one hand and reached down with the other and grasped the boy's little arm. Water rose up to Francis' knees as he gave a mighty tug and pulled the child out of the river. Silver Fox was standing sturdy against the flow of the water and Francis reached his other hand down to get a better hold on the boy and pull him up onto the seat of the saddle.

The Baileys, all screaming during the ordeal, hollered for joy. Herbert, who had stopped pushing his horses forward when he heard his son fall into the water, smiled widely and again snapped the reins to urge his horses onward.

On the other side of the river, Francis led Silver Fox to the moving wagon. The boy was coughing and sputtering, but would obviously survive. Francis passed him off to his mother, who sat in the back of the wagon.

Tears were streaming down her face. "God bless you, Bishop!" she said to him. "God bless you!"

Francis smiled, but shouts along the riverbank drew his attention.

"Over there!" Rodney Yates was pointing upstream. The two Indians flanking them to the north were halfway across the river. It was much deeper at that spot, reaching nearly to their horses' shoulders, so they were moving slowly.

"Like sittin' ducks," Ken Ames said. "I can't shoot a man like that, even a murderin' Injun."

He took off at a run upstream, but as he got closer, one of the Indians pulled an arrow from his quiver and took aim.

"Watch out!" Rodney warned.

"Don't you do that, boy!" Ken called. But as the last word escaped his lips, the arrow came flying directly at him. Ken jumped to the right and lost his footing on the riverbank.

By that time, the other Indian was drawing back his bow, with another arrow aimed directly at Ken, who struggled to stand up.

Pop!

At the sound, Ken looked up and saw the Indian who was drawing his bow crumple over and clutch his stomach. Grabbing hold of his horse's mane, he turned his horse away and headed upstream.

The Indian who had fired the first arrow was a couple of feet from the riverbank now. Occupied with controlling his horse up the steep embankment, he was unable to arm himself. When he finally reached land, he put an arrow to the bow.

"Don't do it, son." Ken Ames stood not ten yards away, aiming his long rifle at him. "Don't make me kill you."

As Francis watched the scene unfold, he guessed the Indian couldn't be more than eighteen or twenty years old.

Deciding to save his own life, the Indian turned his horse to the north toward where his comrade was riding upstream, away from the fight.

Ken shook his head and turned around. Looking at Rodney, he asked, "You shot the other one?"

Rodney nodded solemnly.

"You're one of those I call 'my own,' Ken."

The moment was broken by gunfire.

Rodney, Ken and Francis all retreated to the wagons, which were now all on the west side of the river and in a pattern roughly resembling a circle.

All nine riflemen had crossed the river. Zachary Cloyd had turned his wagon facing parallel to the river and gotten his family out and behind it. It now stood as a barricade, behind which the armed men could stand.

"Fire at will!" Carl told the men.

The Indian raiding party had dismounted their horses and were behind trees on the other side. Every few seconds one or two of them would lean out and release an arrow. Doyng! One hit the frame of the wagon not two feet from where Francis stood, praying. Looking behind him, he noticed the women and children peaking out from their wagons that were standing in a small clearing a short distance away.

Francis climbed aboard Silver Fox and rode swiftly to join them. Several of the men, those who were unarmed, were there as well and Francis found Elijah White peering out between two wagons. He was holding his wife Mildred tightly to him.

"Elijah, Mildred, are you praying?" Francis asked, dismounting Silver Fox.

They turned at his voice but both sets of eyes went to the ground. Just then, Billy Pickens ran up from behind them.

"Bishop. Bishop!"

Francis pulled the boy close to him, out of harm's way, then turned his attention back to Elijah and Mildred. "Beloved, I've told you the greatest weapons we carry. What are they?"

"The Word of God, sir," Elijah answered.

"Then use that Word, Elijah!"

"But what Word?" Elijah nearly pleaded the question.

Francis thought for a moment. Then said: "'If God is for us, who can be against us?'"

Billy chimed in. "And 'The Lord will give His angels charge over you, to keep you in all your ways.'"

"Right, Billy! And 'Terror will be far removed. It will not come near you.'"

Billy again spurted out, "'A thousand may fall at your side, ten thousand at your right hand, but it will not come near you.'"

Francis smiled down at his young protégé and added: "'Confuse the wicked, O Lord. Confound their speech.'

"'Then my enemies will turn back when I call for help. By this I will know that God is for me.'"

"Yes, sir," Elijah said. "That's what we'll pray. Mildred?" His wife looked up at him and nodded, and, holding each other tight, they started praying up a storm.

Francis pulled Billy aside. "Billy, why aren't you with your parents?"

"My Dad! My Dad!" he cried. "He's been wounded!"

Billy pointed back to the semicircle of wagons another forty yards behind them. Francis climbed aboard Silver Fox, helped Billy up behind him, and rode to the far wagons. As they rode, Billy said, "He caught an arrow."

"From way back there?" Francis asked.

"No, from over there," Bill said and pointed to their left. "Came from an Indian in the woods out there."

Francis remembered the Indian who was trying to flank them to the south and determined it must have been he. No one had spotted him while he got all the way to the back of the wagon train.

"How bad is he?" Francis asked.

"It hit across his shoulder," Billy said. "Hurts bad!"

When they reached the wagons, Francis and Billy dismounted and ran to where Ted Pickens was lying with his head propped on a coat. Ted was biting down on a piece of rope while Harriett poured whiskey from a bottle onto his shoulder.

It was all Ted could to do hold back a scream of pain.

Harriett looked up at Francis with tears in her eyes. "Twas the hand of God the arrow didn't pierce him," she said. "Skimmed right across his shoulder blade."

She touched a linen cloth tenderly across the wound, which was about six inches long.

"Phew!" Francis almost lost his breath at the sight and envisioning how close that arrow had come to killing his friend.

Gunshot sounds came from the riverbank and they all turned their attention to the sound. But at the same moment, Kyle Ames, Ken's brother, stepped out of a thicket of trees to the south. A hatchet hung in his hand and blood dripped from its blade.

Francis looked at him questioningly.

"True, I don't got no rifle. But I'm handy 'nough with this here hatchet, Mister Asbury. Good 'nough to get the Injun that tried t'kill Ted here."

Francis nodded agreement, then hung his head in regret that some human beings died with hate in their hearts and would burn eternally in the stifling hot flames of hell.

More gunfire interrupted his thoughts.

A few moments later a cheer arose from the men at the riverbank.

"What's happenin'?" Ted gasped.

All the men, women and children hiding behind the wagons looked in that direction.

"The men are all raising their arms in victory," said Deborah Bailey. She turned to her husband, Herbert, and hugged him.

"The Indians must've left," Francis said.

Gingerly, they all walked around the wagons and started walking tentatively toward the Laurel River.

At the riverbank Carl told Douglas, Zedekiah, William and Levi to stay and keep watch while the others in the wagon train made haste to get as much distance as possible between them and the Indians. Perhaps the Indians would return with reinforcements. Then Carl and the other riflemen escorted Elijah and Mildred White's wagon toward the other wagons and their friends.

"Hallelujah!" Carl shouted as the two groups neared one another. "They've turned back—and we didn't lose one single man or woman in the battle."

There were hugs all around. Several of the children milled around, paying special attention to the rifles.

"What a big bang that makes!" little Sarah Clay said to Carl, pointing to his rifle.

"You know, Miss Clay, I think the big difference in this fight was the big bang of everyone's prayers, not necessarily these rifles."

•••••

The whole wagon train made haste, and covered a great distance for two weeks until they reached Fort Boonesborough on the Kentucky River. Along the way, some found places that to them resembled heaven and they decided to stay and build there. The Belchers and Clays here. The Ingles and Andersons there.

But the saddest farewell Francis had was when Ted and Harriett Pickens, along with Billy, pulled out of the wagon train at Boone on the Roundstone River. It was the second village named Boone that they had passed, and Francis wondered how many more hamlets were named for the famed pioneer.

Billy was riding on the back of the saddle behind Francis, and Francis was telling him of the days he walked the hills and dales of England as a sixteen-year-old, leaving his parents' cottage in Hamstead Valley and helping James Glassbrook, who was a circuit rider for the territory, and preaching five times a week.

"Long, hard days, but fulfilling, Billy."

"I want to do that, Bishop!"

"Do you?"

Billy nodded enthusiastically, then, realizing Francis could not see him, blurted out, "Oh, yes!"

"First, you must count the cost."

"Cost? Do I have to pay to do it?—I will!"

"No, not that kind of cost," Francis laughed. "The spiritual cost, though I'd say that is the great reward, not cost—seeing folks saved, helping deliver people from sins that would lead them to the hot fires of Hades. The financial cost because this is a life without comforts and pleasantries, let alone one that puts money in your pocket. Your best friend becomes your horse."

Francis patted Silver Fox on the neck. "Right, girl?"

The horse snorted.

"Sure sounds difficult, sir," Billy said.

"Yes, Billy. The personal cost is great because there are hungry days and cold nights. Sometimes you never get dry. Many days you never get sleep. Perhaps the greatest cost of all is being unsettled—for you, your family and those who *would* be family.

"Would be?"

"Is a wife in your future, Billy?"

"Dunno. I hope so. Do you got one?"

Francis shook his head sadly, Emily's pretty face flashing before him.

"If you're dreaming of a wife, then this is no life for you, or for the pretty girl in those dreams, Master Pickens."

"Why not, Bishop?"

"You could hardly expect a woman to possess grace enough to enable her to live but one week out of the fifty-two with her husband, could you, Billy?"

The teenager looked quizzically at the back of Francis' head. Francis, knowing so, continued. "If you have a wife and a home, you must run to your dears every night. They are your loves, whom you must protect, provide and care for. And there's no doing that and keeping up with God's work at the same time. Reading, alone, consumes four or five hours a day of my time, Billy, let alone the hours of prayer. What's left is for traveling and preaching—and a handful of hours to sleep."

Billy lowered his head dejectedly.

Francis went on. "What right has any man to take advantage of the affections of a woman, make her his wife, and by a voluntary absence subvert the whole order and economy of the marriage state? Neither God, nature, nor the requirements of society demand that a man and wife be separated so long. It's neither just nor generous."

"Yo!" A man stepped out from the riverside in front of them and waved. "Are the Pickenses with you?"

Carl, riding in front of Francis and Billy, had no time to respond before Ted Pickens, standing on top of the second wagon from the lead, screamed: "Yahoo! Andrew, we're here!"

"Uncle Andrew!" Billy called. "My uncle, Bishop!" he said in Francis' ear and jumped down from Silver Fox. "Uncle Andrew!" he hollered again and ran to the man before them.

Andrew leaned down and hugged the lad. "My, you've grown, boy!" he said. He took a step back and looked Billy over from head to toe. "Look at you!"

Several minutes later, before departing, Billy came back to Francis and said: "I want to be an evergreen tree, Bishop, not a tree that shows leaves only when the weather is good."

Francis dismounted Silver Fox, hugged Billy, then put his hands on his shoulders and looked the boy in the eye. "Then an evergreen tree you'll be, Master Pickens."

Yes, look at you, Billy, Francis thought as he recalled that moment. *A fine young man who loved God, but counted the cost of itinerant preaching too high. Another would-be preacher lost.*

But the thought flittered away like a bubble in the wind as he recalled the scores of young men who filled his life as his "children," whom he had taught and ordained. He had meditated often on Paul's homeless life, the wife that he never named, the children that he never had. Against instincts that beat softly in his heart, he had forsaken father and mother and child and wife, for

Christ's dear sake. He felt Jesus was his family. His Lord's great love became the better substitute for his unmade hearthstone.

He had spiritual compensations, too. God gave him many spiritual children. He felt he was like Paul with a conference of Timothys!

•••••

Abigail Brackett rose from the table. "Another cup of tea, Francis?"

Francis looked down at his cup of tea gone cool and nodded assent.

Just then Thomas burst through the door.

"Bishop! Bishop!" he said, running up to stand before him.

"Master Brackett, you scutter about like a pea on a hot skillet! What is it, my boy?"

"Is preachin' fun?"

Francis smiled. "Exhilarating."

"Ex—exil—ra." Thomas struggled with the word.

"Exciting," Francis said.

"Yeah?"

"Yeah. Seeing the hardest men's hearts melt? It's the best feeling on earth."

"Their hearts actually melt? How do they stay alive?"

"That means their hearts change," Abigail laughed. She poured from a tea kettle into Francis' cup and then Nicholas'.

"Sam?" she asked, looking at her husband.

"Yes. Thank you, dear."

Francis turned a questioning eye to Thomas. "Why do you ask such a question, young Master Brackett?"

Thomas' face lit up. "Just 'cause I might wanna do it when I grow up."

"And a fine preacher you'd be!" Francis said. "You agree, don't you, Nicholas?"

Nicholas smiled. "Indeed!"

"What happened to Billy?" Abigail asked Francis.

"In the end, he counted the cost and the cost was, indeed, too high." Francis shook his head in sadness.

"You met up with Poythress, then?" Sam asked.

"Yes, at Fort Boonesborough. What an achievement that fort was for the pioneers. And what a triumph Poythress had begun!"

Francis flashed back to the late afternoon when his dwindling party arrived at Fort Boonesborough. Richard Henderson, head of the Transylvania Company, which had purchased land from the Cherokees in the Treaty of Sycamore Shoals, had named the fort in honor of Daniel Boone—and it was impressive for being in such wilderness. Trees had been felled to some distance from the fort, so that attackers would have to traverse open space before reaching the fort, except on the back wall, which paralleled the Kentucky River. Those trees were cut to five-yard lengths and these now constituted the walls. Two of the walls were more than two hundred yards long, half-again longer than the other two walls. Entrance gates were placed halfway along each of the longer walls. Blockhouses stood sentinel at the four corners of the fort, peering over the top of the walls like protectors. Tiny windows allowed rifles to poke out and take aim, while giving attackers the most minute targets.

When Carl announced himself and the others in the wagon train, the gates were opened. After fearing Indian attack for most of their entire trip, the gates of Fort Boonesborough might well have been the Gates of Heaven. Safety lay within its walls.

Once inside, the travelers saw that they were not alone in this feeling. Perhaps a hundred settlers milled around the expanse of the fort, taking refuge there during the nights while building their cabins outside during the days. Their numbers explained why the fort enclosed so much space.

The long back wall of the fort contained ten cabins, the shorter walls five cabins on each. Stockades rose behind each of the blockhouses, and one large common building stood in the middle of the fort, partially in the shade of one monstrous oak tree.

Francis could sense the trauma that had taken place inside and outside the four walls of this backwoods fortress.

It had not mattered that the land was purchased from Indians. Other tribes had attacked it since 1775. Not only had scores of settlers been killed, but Daniel Boone's own daughter had been captured in July 1776, along with the two other daughters of another famous pioneer, Richard Calloway. A party of men tracked the Indians, surprised them at their campsite, and rescued the girls.

Two years later, pioneers weathered the "Great Siege of Boonesborough." Earlier, in January, Boone had led thirty men to gather salt at the Lower Blue Licks, where they were captured by Shawnees, taken to Chillicothe in Ohio and eventually back westward. Boone became such a close friend to Chief Blackfish that the Shawnee chief refused to accept the large British reward that was on his head.

Chief Blackfish even adopted Boone, but, in June, Boone slipped away and made his way back to Boonesborough.

That same fall, four hundred Indians and a dozen Frenchmen laid siege to the fort. Furious fighting lasted thirteen days, during which the Indians and French shot fireballs onto the roofs of the cabins to set the place afire. But God was with the pioneers, sending a heavy rainfall to help extinguish the flames.

The report that Francis had read of the siege was that only two pioneers had died and four had been wounded, while nearly forty of the enemy had been killed and a great many wounded.

Yes, this place was already a bastion of legend. And, having faced death and abduction, the people here were rugged, rough, cranky and, Francis found, often vulgar and blasphemous.

Francis was feeling Holy Spirit fire that first night as he looked over the camp and prepared to stand on a wagon somewhere and preach. "It's a hard crowd, Bishop!"

Francis Poythress! Looking somewhat the worse for wear, but a joy to the eyes, Poythresss stretched out his hand toward Francis. Francis grabbed it and the entire arm with it, patting the younger man on the shoulder. "You're here!"

"You expected I wouldn't be?" Poythress asked.

"God willing, I *thought* you might be here. I see that God *was* willing!"

Francis introduced Poythress to Carl and the other nine men who had traveled this long distance, several leaving families behind, to protect him on this journey: Zedekiah, William, Levi, Martin, Jackson, Douglas, Ted, Jacob and Arthur. After resting for a couple of days, Carl and his comrades set out to return home, feeling somewhat assured that Francis and Poythress would be safe.

Safe they were, while having captive audiences for day-and-night preaching. Callous men, worn-out women, frosty children— all listened, some fervently, many only with mild interest but finding it at least a way to pass the time—an entertainment of sorts.

After a time, Poythress and Francis, with their horses and a packhorse, took to the Kentucky forests, and on up the Ohio River Valley, here and there finding ramshackle structures filled with one, sometimes two families; persuading sinners, and nurturing believers.

Oftentimes, they slept with families in their one-room cabins. Other times, the homes were so cramped that they slept in the woods, annoyed by disagreeable bugs, showing them the necessity of crying to the Lord for patience.

One night, lying in the woods, their heads resting on their saddlebags, Poythress asked, "Frank, do you ever wonder what on earth we're doing out here in this wilderness? These people in the mountains and backwoods settlements are so uncouth and wicked, I sometimes feel as though we dwell as among briars, thorns and scorpions!"

"Let me read you something," Francis said. Sitting up, he took hold of a pamphlet at his side. "This was written by James Meikle, the surgeon and preacher:

> 'Do not only press charity on the wealthy;
> but let your example, according to your ability,
> show the way. Lend your ear to reproaches,
> rather than applauses. Reproaches may let

us see some of our foibles or failings. But commendation is very apt to kindle self-conceit, of which everyone has enough. Seek not great things for yourself. Seek not great fame, great applause, great comforts, or a great income. But seek great things for Christ. Seek for Him great glory, many converts, and much fruits of righteousness. Consider the preciousness of souls, the value of salvation, the weight of the sacred charge, the terrors of the Almighty, the solemn day of judgment, and your own utter inability. Then shall you have no vain confidence, but depend on God alone.'"

Francis put down the pamphlet and turned to Poythress. "I'd say we're fulfilling the call: no great fame, or applause, comforts or income, but many converts and fruit of righteousness."

But another time, Francis suffered that same morose feeling. They had been traveling several days and happened upon only a few. He felt he was bearing no fruit. Then, in the midst of the Western wilderness, they came upon a rude log chapel in the woods and found they had entered a love feast on Sabbath morning. They quietly settled into seats at the back of the room, unknown to anyone in the congregation.

The preacher waded through some preliminary exercises, relating to the goings-on in the little village and his church. Then he asked for people to relate their Christian experiences. One after another, they testified of the saving grace of God. Occasionally, one of the members rose and sang a hymn. It was touching. The Holy Spirit was moving among these people and Francis was reminded of the Scripture, "We overcome the enemy by the blood of the Lamb and the words of our testimony."

While hearts were rising and swelling, a plain but exceedingly neatly attired lady arose.

"I have traveled many miles to this meeting," she declared in a full and clear, though slightly tremulous, voice, "and my feelings will not allow me to repress my testimony. I have not long been a follower of Christ.

"Two years ago, I was attracted to a Methodist meeting in our neighborhood by being informed that Bishop Asbury was going to preach."

Francis sat forward.

"I went," the lady continued, "and the Spirit sealed the truth He uttered on my heart. I fled to Jesus and found redemption in IIis blood, even the forgiveness of my sins. Ever since then, I've been happy in His love!"

Then she sang: "'Not a cloud doth arise to darken my skies / or hide for a moment my Lord from my eyes.'"

Francis rose to his feet. "I'm a stranger and pilgrim, halting on his way for rest and refreshment in the house of God, and I've found both!"

When he and Poythress went on their way that day, he lifted his hands to the sky and tears of joy coursed down his face. Atop his horse, he looked at Poythress beside him. "If I can only be instrumental in the conversion of one soul in traveling around the continent, I will travel around till I die. This morning has been a Godsend, an appointment from the Lord—for both of us, Poythress. Do you see that?"

Poythress smiled broadly, "Dear Bishop, our God's timing is perfect, isn't it?"

Suddenly, Francis was back in Scarborough. He looked around at the family and Nicholas. "Oh, how many thousands of poor souls have we to seek out in the wilds of America who are narrowly removed from the Indians in the comforts of civilized society and, considering that they have the Bible in their hands, comparatively worse in their morals than the savages themselves? Like Paul to the Galatians, I'm concerned by the badness of their own hearts, and from their hearing corrupt doctrines."

Sam stood. "Francis, I just realized, if Thomas is home, that means it's getting late. And I've got more work to do in the field. Would you continue when I get back?"

"Of course."

•••••

When Francis, Nicholas and the Bracketts settled down for dinner, Sam pointed at Francis. "So, you've traveled back and forth across the Alleghenies dozens of times?"

Francis nodded. "Silver Fox knew the region well. To the limits of white civilization across the great Mississippi River, the fellowship grew like wildfire. So quickly, we held our first conference west of the Alleghenies in May seventeen hundred eighty-eight in the upper room of Stephen Keywood's log house in Glade Spring, Virginia.

"And what a conference! Days of preaching! It led to the conversion of General William Russell, a Revolutionary War hero, and his wife, Elizabeth, sister to Patrick Henry. Though it wasn't our plan, winning the heart and souls of prominent citizens like them greatly helped our cause."

Francis had yet to visit some of the farthest territories, but had sent missionaries as far as the land was opened for settlements.

In 1786 he assigned James Haw and Benjamin Ogden as the first traveling preachers in Kentucky. A year later, they reported ninety conversions to the faith.

Francis remembered, in 1793, sending Joseph Lillard into Illinois to form the first Methodist society in the state.

And after General Anthony Wayne made the Treaty of Greenville with the Wyandots, Delawares, Chippewas and other Indian tribes northwest of the Ohio River in 1795, Francis reinforced the territory with stationed preachers and evangelists and formed circuits and districts.

Francis took a bite of tasty chicken breast that Abigail had cooked and looked around the dinner table. "God gave Tom Coke and me a wonderful strategy: send out preachers with fanatical zeal to sow the seed and then send in preachers possessing skills in organization and administration. The first ones would whip those pioneers in the wilderness territories into such a religious passion that it could help them survive the mighty trials they faced. No small faith would work. *You* know that." Francis said the last sentence with firmness, knowing the Bracketts and their neighbors stood daily against the dangers of enemies as well as the storms of nature.

Sam and Abigail both nodded agreement.

"These men I sent westward, many had convinced themselves that the harsher their physical hardship and emotional torment, the brighter they would shine in the eyes of their Lord. As I told brother Daniel Hitt, I was happy to find God's reviving of the west through the great works of these men and His Holy Spirit.

"It was all proof that God has a controversy with this land. Many that will not be mended will be ended, or mended and ended both!" An eyebrow rose as Francis looked at Nicholas. "Remember this, son: America is the infant of divine Providence and we preachers sit in a very hot seat. Judgment begins in the house of the Lord. And when God begins His correction, He'll correct us Himself. He'll not let others do it."

"Men with 'fanshical zeal'?" Thomas said from a stool beside Francis.

"Yes, Thomas, fanatical zeal." Francis patted the boy on the shoulder. "That means men who are dedicated, enthusiastic, passionate and devoted to God."

"Who's the biggest?"

"Biggest?"

"Yeah, who has the most?"

"Oh, only God knows for sure. He's the only One who knows our heart."

"How about the most memorable?" Sam said.

"Memorable?" Francis rubbed his chin, spooned a dollop of potato into his mouth, and repeated, "Memorable."

"Who won't you forget?" Thomas said, trying to help.

Francis laughed. "Oh, I know the meaning of the word, thank you, Thomas. I was just thinking. So many dedicated people. Some have died because of that commitment."

"Died!?"

"Yes, died." A light went on in his memory, and it sprang from Francis' lips. "Lorenzo Dow."

"Lorenzo Dow," Nicholas said, his voice rising in recognition.

"I've never heard the name," Sam said.

"Me, either," Abigail agreed.

"It's been said," Nicholas interjected, "that few could so graphically depict the horrors of hell and the wonders of heaven as Lorenzo Dow."

Francis nodded agreement. "A few moments of Lorenzo's preaching and a house full of sober settlers could transform into a trembling mob of screamers. Some suspected he was simply borderline insane—and they had reason to think so. Unshaven. Unshorn. His hair fell below his shoulders and his whiskers reached almost to his waist. Wearing torn and shabby clothing. Tall and thin, he would go without sleep and food—except perhaps a few grasshoppers—until he was emaciated and cadaverous, and then he'd show up on some poor woman's doorstep, knock on the door and nearly scare her to death when she looked upon him.

"Here was this gaunt, hairy man kneeling with his hands clasped and his eyes turned toward heaven and crying, 'A crust! A crust for a Methodist preacher!'"

Thomas giggled and the others laughed uncomfortably.

Francis shrugged. "But I believed there was more to him. The piercing eyes, the hard word, perhaps a prophet—a word reminiscent of Elijah calling for repentance. I assigned him to Alabama and the reports I received were that his converts were vigorous for the truth; solid Bereans.

"Set aside the looks and clothing, and Lorenzo was the perfect specimen for whipping people into a godly frenzy, setting the stage for others who are strong organizers—men who could consolidate the holy positions that had been won, settle the societies, encourage the building of chapels, and prepare that territory for Methodist Conferences as organized circuits and working units of the church."

Francis shook his head in remembrance. "And one other thing."

"What's that?" Sam asked.

"I wasn't concerned that he'd get married."

"Concerned?" Abigail asked.

Francis nodded. "My preachers flock to the altar as readily as they save souls, and with the same success!"

Nicholas laughed.

Francis gave him a stern look and he quickly realized this was a serious topic for his mentor.

"Despite our preachers' poverty and the uncertainty of life with them, women desire to marry them," Francis said, "and they've done so every year—and in large numbers."

"Does this have to do with the notion that marrying a preacher guarantees heaven?" Abigail asked.

"Yes," Francis said, "a widely held heresy."

He shook his head in disbelief.

"It's been especially difficult in a certain large Virginia circuit where, for some reason, the women are greatly in the majority and particularly avid in their search for husbands. All my circuit riders there have been married within a few months after receiving their assignments and immediately request permanent location."

Francis laughed despite himself, "I—I even sent two decrepit old men into the district, believing that the women would not attempt to lure them, of all people, to the altar. As husbands—not as evangelists, mind you—they left much to be desired."

"What happened?" Sam asked.

"Within a year they were both married!"

Everyone laughed. Finally, Francis declared, "The devil and the women will get all my preachers."

CHAPTER 10

Defying Yellow Fever

"I suppose, Francis," Sam said, "that those trips across the mountains and into Indian territory, and up in the woods here with Indians and highwaymen about, have been the scariest."

Francis chewed slowly on a forkful of deer meat. He was pondering his answer. "Whatever you do with this venison is beyond delicious, Abigail," he said.

"Thank you," Abigail said. "Must be the apple trees hereabouts that they thrive on. Makes for sweet meat."

"Well, dear, you're a sweet hostess, so it's a fitting meal."

Abigail smiled.

"'Scary' is a word I try to avoid, Sam," Francis said, "but I do admit to staring the most frightening fear in the face. And, I believe, it was not in the woods wondering if a pack of Indians was about to murder us and skin us alive."

"What could be scarier than that, Bishop?" Thomas asked.

"Yellow fever, young Thomas. Yellow fever."

Francis remembered his first meeting with the killer. It started when he encountered those who were fleeing from it. It was in the heat of the summer in 1793—incredibly hot, unusually dry—as he rode toward Philadelphia from the south. He was fanning his face with his hat and wasn't for a moment missing the coat that he had given away to a poor vagabond miles back.

Several miles outside the city, riding along the highway, he approached a number of families. Some were on foot, others on horses. Some were pulling little carts themselves, others' carts were horse drawn. Men and women in buggies. Children sitting atop wagons.

"Bishop!" The voice sounded vaguely familiar.

"Mister Asbury!" came another call.

Two little girls, perhaps ten and twelve years old, hopped from a wagon and bounded toward him. The older girl, her long blonde hair flying behind, waved her hands over her head in a motion for him to stop.

He pulled Silver Fox to a halt.

"Don't go, Bishop!" she said. "Don't go!"

"Don't go where, Madeliene?"

"Philadelphia."

"And why not?"

"They're all dyin'!"

Francis looked up to see the girls' parents, Jedekiah and Melissa Goss.

"Yellow fever, Bishop," Jedekiah explained from his perch atop the wagon. "Killin' fifty, a hundred a day."

Francis' jaw dropped. Fifty to one hundred dying! Every day!

"Mayor Clarkson's told everyone to leave the city," said Melissa, sitting beside her husband. "Mister Washington and members of his Cabinet, as well as Mister Jefferson and other members of the federal government are all debating whether they should leave and set up government in Germantown."

"What brought this on?" Francis asked.

"They're just guessin'," Jedekiah said. "Some say it's this weather causing stagnant water to be putrid and carry disease."

"Some say it's the noxious fumes from blocked sewers," Melissa said.

"Or rotten cargo on the waterfront," Jedekiah said.

"And some say the city needs a bath!" called little Madeline from beside Silver Fox.

"And a lot are sayin' it's contagion from all the Santo

Domingans flocking into Philadelphia," Melissa said, tossing aside a strand of hair from her face.

Francis had heard of the Santo Domingans fleeing an island rebellion. White, black, rich, poor—it was a diverse group, and many Americans were very suspicious of them.

"It's a horrible disease, wherever it comes from," said Jedekiah.

"Nausea," said Melissa.

"Black vomiting," added Jedekiah.

"Yuck!" Madelene said, and held her hand up to Francis. He pulled her up to sit on his saddle.

"Me, too!" cried her sister, Adalia, lifting up her arms. Francis took ahold of her hands and placed her gently behind him, so the little girls were in front and behind him. Madeline tugged at his shirt and Adalia pulled at his bedsack.

"Girls, stop it!" Jedekiah snapped. "Leave the bishop alone," he hesitated as a smile curled his lips. "At least while we're talkin'."

"As we said," Melissa said, "nausea, black vomiting, yellow skin....

"High fever causing delirium," Jedekiah added.

"Severe sensitivity," Melissa said.

"Even hiccups!" declared Madeline, crossing her arms with determination.

Somewhere in the background Francis heard someone call out, "It's Bishop Asbury, everyone! The Bishop's here!" Moments later, people in other wagons and buggies were pulling up and were listening to the conversation.

"They're quarantining ships, too, Bishop," said one man. Francis looked over to see another familiar face—that of Thaddeus Boehm.

"Good idea," Francis said. "Coming and going both, I'd hope." He thought for a moment. "If the mayor is asking people to leave, is there no cure?"

"Doctor Benjamin Rush and his circle are mostly prescribing heroic bleeding and purging," said Thaddeus.

"But there's a doctor from Santo Domingo who's having better luck giving doses of quinine and stimulants," said Jedekiah.

"His name's Doctor Jean Devéze," joined in Thaddeus' wife, Helen, "and that's the same treatment that cured Alexander and Betsey Hamilton."

"Mister Hamilton and his wife had the fever and survived?" Francis asked.

Helen nodded.

"God must have something planned for them," Jedekiah said.

"God has something planned for all of us, Jedekiah," Francis replied. "What are your plans? Where are you heading?"

"Away, Bishop. Away."

"Til God says, 'Stop,'" Melissa said.

"Are you sure God said, 'Go'?" Francis asked.

Madeline looked blankly back at him. After a moment, she answered, "The mayor said, 'Go.'"

Francis simply nodded and saw the conviction, almost shock, on her face as she realized the meaning of his question.

"Is anyone staying behind?" he asked.

"Many are, yes," said Thaddeus, "to minister to the sick and, it being the national capital as well as the state capital, to make sure the city doesn't collapse."

"My friend Wilhemina's staying with her family," Melissa piped up.

Francis patted her head. "And why is that, dear heart?"

"She's African and they're *all* stayin'," the girl replied.

"Truly?"

"Truly," she replied firmly.

"Bishop," said Jedekiah, "city officials have asked Pastor Allen if the African community will stay and nurse those who are sufferin' and help bury the dead."

"Ha!" Francis said. "Sounds like 'city officials' count the black people less worthy of living!"

"No-no, sir," Jedekiah said. "For some reason, the Africans aren't affected by the yellow fever."

"But," Thaddeus said, "Matthew Carey published a pamphlet

accusing the blacks of profiting financially from the fever by overcharging for burying the dead and by stealing from the houses they entered. But Mayor Clarkson and Pastor Allen took out ads in newspapers denouncing Carey's accusations."

"A scourge, that Carey!" Francis said. "This Pastor Allen—is that Richard Allen?"

"Yessir," Thaddeus said.

Francis smiled. As far back as 1781, he had made sure that the fiery Allen, a former slave saved under Freeborn Garretson, had ample opportunities to preach. Since returning in 1786 to Philadelphia, where he joined St. George's Methodist Episcopal Church, Allen's leadership at prayer services had attracted dozens of Africans into the church.

With them came increased racial tension, but Francis acknowledged those feelings needed to be addressed. Negro pews? African corners? Separate cemeteries? This wasn't right. Right was blacks and whites worshiping side by side, arm in arm, not segregated to particular parts of the same building.

"A man after my own heart," Francis said. Hugging the girls before and behind him, he declared, "Dear hearts, I must be gone." With that, he hoisted the girls to the ground, bade farewell and good fortune to the crowd leaving the city, and rode off toward Philadelphia, yellow fever and, well, he knew not what.

•••••

The closer Francis got to the heart of Philadelphia, the more frenetic its streets became. Francis' head was spinning. What was he riding into? He simply had to go. The choice was similar to that made when he decided to stay in America during the Revolutionary War. Did he retreat then and give over victory to Satan? No. Should he shrink from this "war" now? Indeed not!

Children screamed in the streets. Here and there, women wailed behind closed doors. Here and there, a well-dressed man carrying a medical bag rushed by.

Asking along the way, Francis found his way to the temporary asylum that had been prepared for the sick on Bush Hill, a commandeered mansion on the outskirts of the city.

He tethered Silver Fox outside and entered the wide front doors of the manor. The scene was horrific. Men and women, boys and girls, rich and poor—no matter their background—had been struck by the yellow fever and were lying on cots side by side. Moans and groans filled the air. There was the pungent odor of—death.

Mayor Clarkson appeared around a doorway and strode to Francis. "Bishop!" He held out his hand.

"Matthew." Francis gripped his hand, then locked his eyes on the man. Clarkson appeared disheveled and tired.

"You need your rest, Matthew."

"You need to leave town, Bishop!"

"You know that won't happen. If indeed God called me to minister, do I run in the face of yellow fever, or any other thing, for that matter? No, my calling's more precious to me than that. Death will come when it will come, Matthew."

"You sound like Pastor Allen!"

"I'm honored to sound like him." Francis hesitated. "Where may I find him?"

Clarkson pointed to the top of a stairway. "One of those rooms."

Before stepping off toward the staircase, Francis grabbed Clarkson's elbow. "Does it appear Mister Franklin, God bless his soul, was correct in wanting a source of clean, fresh and flowing water in the city instead of your hodgepodge of wells, cisterns and springs?"

Clarkson shrugged and nodded. "Engineers are planning a water works as we speak, Bishop. We're putting to use the thousand-pound bequest Mister Franklin left to the city to build a new water system."

"Good. Now get some rest, Matthew," Francis said and walked off.

As Francis ascended the staircase he heard wailing and loud moaning. It got louder the closer he got to the top. People were in torturous fever. At the top of the stairs, he turned right and was startled by the sight. Cots by the score, side by side with barely two feet between them, lined the hallway. More cots filled each of the rooms to the left and right.

Some people were merely staring into space, but others were obviously feverish. Black men and women hurried about with bowls of water, towels or blankets, some of them stopping to cool the fever of a patient by dipping a cloth in cool water and wiping their brow; others wiped perspiration from the heads of those lying down.

It was a nightmare of the worst degree.

Francis asked one of the African men where he could find Pastor Allen and he pointed to the far corner of a room.

As Francis approached him, Pastor Allen noticed him. And as he drew nearer still, his face lit up. "Frank!"

Francis took stock of the handsome man before him. Thirty-ish, with receding, black curly hair, close-cropped ears and a strong face, he carried himself with dignity. His high spirits and charisma were unmistakable. In 1789, when the Free African Society adopted various Quaker practices, such as having fifteen minutes of silence at its meetings, Allen had led a withdrawal of those who preferred more enthusiastic Methodist practices. He succumbed to no peer pressure.

Francis reached him, walked through the extended handshake and hugged him. "As always, Richard," he said, "I see you're standing against the storm. If it's not one thing, it's another, eh?"

Richard smiled wryly. "This is a most difficult tempest, Frank. And, in many ways, very revealing."

"Revealing? In what ways?"

"Well, I find it interesting, for instance, that some of the same people who wanted all of us blacks to leave America for Sierra Leone on the west coast of Africa, are now even more happy for us to stay here in Philadelphia...."

"And care for their own families," Francis finished.

Richard nodded. "Husbands are abandoning sick wives, parents are leaving children, hysterical with fear that death will claim them as well!" Richard said. "The mayor asks the African community to stay, to nurse, to drive the death carts, to dig the graves and bury the dead. To prove ourselves morally equal to those who have reviled us, we've dedicated ourselves to working with the sick, and what's the response? Matthew Carey denounces us!"

"I heard," Francis said. "But don't let that man, or others, plant a seed of hate, or unforgiveness, or bitterness in your heart, Richard. Indignation, perhaps. But don't let it seep deeper than that."

Richard nodded agreement. "You're right, but it is difficult."

"What do you think is the cause of the fever?" Francis asked.

"Sin. The diseased moral condition of the people. Why do you think people call Philadelphia the 'Athens of America'?"

Before Francis could reply, Richard resumed, "They may think it is because its inhabitants are the educated, the rich, the famous, the favored. But why did ancient Greece die, Frank?"

"Sin."

"Exactly. And I believe that, like Sodom and Gomorrah, what we're witnessing here is God's judgment."

•••••

Preaching at Ebenezer Church that night, Francis paraphrased Micah 6:9: "Listen! The Lord is calling to the city—and to fear Your name is wisdom—'Heed the rod and the One Who appointed it.'"

"Ah, how the ways mourn! How low-spirited are the people while making their escape! I saw it in their eyes, heard it in their voices, felt it in my spirit as I approached the city today.

"Poor Philadelphia! This lofty city, He layeth it low."

He looked about the congregation. There wasn't a seat left to sit in. Whites mingled with the black church members, something they obviously were not used to doing, but something they acquiesced to just to hear the bishop.

He asked, "Do we here think this yellow fever has happened

simply because of squalid conditions? Do we think peril awaits us for no reason?"

Heads shook throughout the building.

"Yea, in the way of Your judgments have we waited for You, O Lord. Believers who know the scriptures know the admonitions of God to flee from sin of every kind. Old Testament, New Testament, it matters not. God calls to us through His holy Word as a warning to His beloved!"

He picked up his Bible from the podium and found his passage.

"The Old Testament tells us in Deuteronomy thirty, verses fifteen and sixteen: 'See, I have set before you today life and good, death and evil, in that I command you today to love the Lord your God, to walk in His ways, and to keep His commandments, His statutes, and His judgments, that you may live and multiply; and the Lord your God will bless you in the land which you go to possess.'"

Turning to another passage, he continued: "The New Testament tells us in Hebrews chapter ten, verse twenty-six: 'For if we sin willfully after we have received the knowledge of the truth, there no longer remains a sacrifice for sins, but a certain fearful expectation of judgment, and fiery indignation which will devour the adversaries.'

"And in Second Thessalonians chapter one, verse nine, Paul declares, 'These [who do not know God and do not obey the gospel] shall be punished with everlasting destruction from the presence of the Lord and from the glory of His power.'"

Francis set down his Bible and looked intently at one specific white man in the middle of the church. The Spirit of God told Francis the man's heart was ripe for a mighty change.

"Who's in control?" he asked.

Murmurs throughout the room.

"In some circles it's preached that Satan brings the flood and destruction, that God is a God of love and therefore does not cause death or harm," Francis said. "Many concede that, yes, God did destroy in the Old Testament but not since the 'new and better testament.' Wrong!

"Yes, God is love. But if you examine all of Scripture you'll see that God's love can not embrace what His righteousness can not endure. He does not give a stamp of approval to everyone just because He is love.

"We've seen through these scriptures who sends the droughts and flooding. Do you need more texts?"

The white man in the middle squirmed in his seat, thinking to stand and squeeze his way out of the pew.

"Deuteronomy chapter eleven, verse seventeen," Francis' voice boomed. 'Lest the Lord's anger be aroused against you, and He shut up the heavens so that there be no rain, and the land yield no produce, and you perish quickly from the good land which the Lord is giving you.'

"Jeremiah chapter ten, verse thirteen: 'When He utters His voice there is a multitude of waters in the heavens; and He causes the vapors to ascend from the ends of the earth. He makes lightning for the rain. He brings the wind out of His treasures.'

"Psalm one hundred forty-eight, verse eight: 'Fire and hail, snow and clouds; stormy wind, fulfilling His Word.'

"Yes, the Lord brings floods, droughts, ice and snowstorms," Francis continued. "And He also parses out judgments in other ways. Witness that He allowed Moses, Aaron and their entire generation to die without entering Canaan because of their unbelief! The book of Numbers says: 'Aaron shall be gathered to his people, for he shall not enter the land which I have given to the children of Israel, because you rebelled against My Word at the water of Meribah.'

"The Lord took the lives of Ananias and Sapphira for deception in the New Testament.

"And, dear friends, listen to me." Francis hesitated and looked square at the white man in the midst of the congregation. "Look at me and listen! The Lord imparts sickness as a judgment for sin. Yes, He does! Leviticus twenty-six, verse fifteen declares," Francis quickly turned to the page. "It says, 'and if you despise My statutes, or if your soul abhors My judgments, so that you do not perform all My commandments, but break My covenant, I will also do this to you.' The Lord also lists a myriad of actions like allowing their enemies to destroy them and shutting off the land from producing produce or fruit.

"Yes, God sent pestilence, famine, blasting and mildew, and, look here, *only* the church and the people of God know and believe His judgments."

Francis scanned the congregation. "Now, who here does not believe in God's judgments?"

Not one hand was raised.

"Well, know this, then. God's people, who wait for Him in the way of His judgments, may be improved and profited by them!

"Give glory to God before He causes even greater darkness and before your feet stumble upon the blackest of mountains, and before He turns it into the shadow of death and gross darkness!"

Not a whisper could be heard for a moment, two, three. Several seconds passed, and then, "Amen, Bishop! Amen!" Pastor Allen rose to his feet. "Give glory to God, people!"

First one by one, and then pews full of people rose to their feet.

"Glory to God!"

"Glory to God on the highest!"

Francis continued: "Father, as some are dying and others flying tonight, we look inward, inward to inspect our own hearts to see what truly lies there. Please refrain from harsh judgment, Father, and cleanse us, giving us a new start. Cover us with the precious blood of the Lamb, that the disease plaguing this city will not touch your children! Amen."

"Amens" abounded throughout the church and then Pastor Allen bounded up beside Francis and whispered into his ear just loud enough for him to hear above the noise.

Francis nodded agreement and Pastor Allen turned to the church. "Brothers and sisters, we're calling, right this very moment, for a day of fasting and prayer."

"Amen!" came a chorus around the church.

After the Sabbath, others left the city, but Francis remained with Richard, his assistant Absalom Jones, and others, including William Gray, a fruit seller who, along with Allen and Jones, had secured support to build the African Church the previous year. Death reined. A number who suffered, survived, but even some blacks, more than two hundred, succumbed to the plague. Francis stayed on for more than two months, preaching, ministering and praying with the sick, and praying alone with God a dozen times a day. He refused warnings about his health; he'd reply, "I don't remember the last time I felt well myself, what with cold, rheumatism and what-have-you. By God's will, I'll survive."

In September the weather cooled down, the fever lessened and Francis decided he could leave to find out how his circuit riders were faring around the country.

Before leaving the manor, he saw Dr. Rush conferring with Dr. Philip Syng Physick. *Two of the great men of the day*, he thought.

"Gentlemen," Francis said.

"Bishop!" the two men said in unison and put forth their hands. Shaking them both, Francis said, "You're brave men. Great men. Your work here has been incredible."

"You humble me," Rush said.

"Not at all," Francis said. "And, Doctor Physick, here you've cared for Chief Justice Marshall, Dolley Madison, Mister Adams' daughter and countless others...."

"Including me," Rush added.

Physick raised a hand in protest.

"What can I pay for your services?" Francis reached into his coat for his wallet.

"Nothing," Rush said, putting his hand on Francis' wrist.

"Only an interest in your prayers," Physick added.

Francis looked the two men in the eye. "Well, then, as I do not like to be in debt, we'll pray now." He knelt down and the two men joined him in the front foyer to the grand mansion, and prayed fervently, until he felt the heavens open so that God would bless and reward them for their kindness, wisdom and daring in the face of death itself.

As Francis recalled that time, Abigail cut in with the question, "So that was the most fearful time you've encountered?"

"Fearful. Panic-stricken. People were so terrified and unnerved that they lost their wits, they fled from their own spouses and children, they gave themselves over to the will of Satan! And it was the fiercest time that tested men's faith," Francis said. "How do you answer the question of good people dying in so horrible a way?"

Nicholas replied, "Doesn't Jesus allude to the question in Luke chapter thirteen?"

Francis thought for a moment. "About the people who died when the Tower of Siloam fell on them?"

"Yes."

"What happened?" Sam asked.

"How many died?" Thomas piped up.

Francis nodded to Nicholas to tell the story.

"Well, eighteen people died when this tower fell on them, and Jesus asked the Pharisees, 'Do you think that they were more guilty than all the others living in Jerusalem?'"

"Were they?" Thomas asked.

Nicholas shook his head. "No, little man, they were not."

"So what does that tell us?" Abigail asked.

"Well," Nicholas said, "Jesus told the people, 'But unless you repent, you too will all perish.'"

"Then He told a parable about a fig tree that was planted in a vineyard and didn't bear fruit for three years," Francis joined in. "So the owner told the keeper of the vineyard to cut down the fig tree, but the keeper asked that he let it alone for one more year so that he could dig around it and fertilize it. And, he said, "'If it bears fruit the next year, fine! If not, then cut it down.'"

"What did the owner say?" Thomas asked.

"Jesus doesn't tell us that, Thomas," Francis said. "And that's the meaning to the telling of the whole episode—both the tower that Nicholas mentioned and the parable that Jesus told immediately afterward."

Thomas looked quizzically at Francis.

"People will die," Francis said, "even good people. We live in a fallen world, not a perfect world, and we pay the price because of that. Jesus' message here was that we must examine our lives knowing that, inevitably, we will all die. And so we must be ready for that moment. It could be totally unexpected, like those eighteen people who were killed by the Tower of Siloam. It could be a lengthy and torturous time like those who died from yellow fever in Philadelphia. The important question is the eternal one: Have you repented and are you right with God the moment you die? Repentance doesn't immunize us against disease and death, or any other tragedy. But, in turning to Him, we become able to live with life's doubts and fears."

Abigail rose and began cleaning the table. "Tea before church?"

The adults all nodded consent.

"What happened to Pastor Allen and his people?" Sam asked.

"Oh, he's fulfilling his call from God. I joined him a year or two later to dedicate his new church, quoting verses from Genesis relating to Jacob's dream of a ladder to heaven at a place called Bethel. The congregation then named its church 'Mother Bethel.'"

CHAPTER 11

Battling Booze and Unbelief

That night, Francis, Nicholas and the Bracketts again walked to the church together. Little Thomas proudly held Francis' hand. A cool night, it was pleasant both outside and in the log building. After singing several hymns and an opening prayer, Pastor Matthews introduced Francis. People were crammed into every nook and cranny. Many were sitting on the floor in the aisles. Others stood two or three deep along the walls. Still others stuck their heads in the door, straining to hear.

The whole county must be here, Francis thought.

Standing at the pulpit, Francis looked about. Truly these were hard-working people. Determined. Steadfast. Courageous. This was good.

Truly they were sinners. Not one could claim otherwise, not even himself. He knew that well and repented every day for things said and unsaid, done and undone.

Francis picked up his Bible with his right hand and a popular Dorothy Kilner book with his left. "Some say we need to balance the Bible," he looked at the Bible, "with the world."

He looked at the other book.

"Some say necessities of the world mean tossing out the Bible. But I say the necessities of the Bible mean tossing out the world." Francis moved his left arm parallel to the floor and let the novel drop to the ground. The "thud" resounded throughout the room.

"There's a castle in Adair, Ireland, where, etched in large

letters in the stoneworks along the top of the curtain wall, is the scripture, 'Unless the Lord build a thing, they labour in vain who build it.'

"The framers of the Constitution of this young republic recognized that scripture as fact and have, thankfully," Francis held high his Bible, "written our laws using the Bible as their plumb line. They used no novel. No matter their faith, or lack of it, nothing of the base instincts of man played a part in their deliberations."

Francis scanned the church. "Have they done well?"

"Yes!" came a scattering of responses. There was no apparent disagreement.

Francis set the Bible on the pulpit before him and continued. "John Locke, who relies heavily on God's Word, proclaims—and the great framers of our Constitution agree—laws are a 'social contract' in which citizens swap some freedom for a civilized life. Everyone's freedom is curtailed, and everyone benefits. The results are civil society. Law demands that we must not kill. That is an impairment on the will of killers, but it protects the rest of us." People nodded their heads and grinned "*of courses*" to one another.

"Law demands that we not steal. The poor thieves among us must hate that law; but it protects the rest of us."

Again, heads nodded agreement.

"Law demands that we not destroy our neighbor's property. Ah, pity the destructive among us who must live by such a law!" Francis said jokingly.

Laughs met his statement.

"Yet there is no law against intemperance!" Francis raised his voice. People looked up questioningly. What was this about? "A sip of wine, or a glass of ale, I have no trouble with—especially if used for medicinal purposes. Peter even told Timothy to take a little wine, for it was good for his stomach. And Jesus drank wine with His disciples. He even turned water into wine as His first miracle," Francis said. "But wherever I go, and especially in the wilderness parts of our young country, I see overindulgence. Is not one stein of ale enough? Is not one glass of wine enough?"

He looked about at a quiet audience but with heads nodding agreement.

"None other than Mister Benjamin Franklin wrote in *Poor Richard*, 'Nothing more like a fool than a drunken man.'

"Proponents of liquor declare that good whiskey is a blessing from God, to be used accordingly, to be prescribed as a preventive of disease, and necessary to social intercourse. But some families are ready to starve for want of bread, while their fathers and husbands distill corn and rye into poisonous whiskey! I even happened upon a minister who was guilty of the same. I said to him, 'It's no wonder, sir, that you have no compassion for these poor souls under your spiritual care. You have none for your own body!

"So I intend to preach from these northern parts of our country to the most southern, asking for laws diminishing this deadly liquor."

Groans greeted this statement.

Francis went on: "Listen! Every civilized society must be governed in some fashion. The less stringent the government, the more they must have individual self-government, or self-control, if you will. The less public law, the more they must rely on people living with moral self-constraint.

"Somewhere I've read, and I agree, that 'men, in a word, must necessarily be controlled, either by a power within them, or by a power without them; either by the Word of God, or by the strong arm of man; either by the Bible, or by the bayonet.'"

Sam, sitting at the corner of his third pew from the front, winced. He could almost feel the air leave the building in a collective whoosh.

Francis looked about. "Is this not true?"

Pastor Matthews offered a hearty, "Amen," as did Nicholas, Sam and a number of others.

"Tell me if it's not true," Francis said, "that a mind tainted by liquor is susceptible to mingle with the most impure companions. Does not Proverbs chapter thirteen, verse twenty tell us that 'He who walks with the wise grows wise, but a companion of fools suffers harm'?"

"Tell me if it's not true," he said, "that these impaired cohorts are more apt to commit violence.

"Think of the violence perpetrated against individuals, families and society as a whole, and you can most often trace its origins to intemperance. Think how many otherwise rational men it transforms into beasts of prey! How many marriages it warps! How many families it leaves without roof for head, clothes for body, or food for stomach! How otherwise peaceful villages it leaves in ruins!"

Francis took a deep breath and prayed to God for words. A congregation that was so willing just this morning was so much less willing this night.

"Listen to me, dear ones," Francis lowered his voice to a plead. "Where is justice in the wake of intemperance? Is there justice for the victim after injury? The injury's been done. Is there even justice for the drinker? His soul faces ruin! Those who give their lives over to drink succumb to a life of misery!

"The only ones among us who prosper are the dram shops and tippling houses. Am I not correct?"

Heads now slowly started nodding "yes."

"Praise God there are no such places here in Scarborough!" Francis declared. "But—but, dear friends, every such place, wherever it be, is a prevailing evil in this land, a breeder of murder and a force driving the drinker toward the eternal wrath of God and eternal ruin of the man. We think it inconsistent with the character of a Christian to be immersed in the practice of distilling or retailing an article so destructive to the morals of society. This evil has ruined thousands, both in time and eternity!"

As Abigail snuggled close to him, Sam shook his head in wonderment. Every stroke from Francis' mouth was like a dagger to the hilt. Even the innocent felt the prick.

"This I tell you, dear friends, because you are beloved of God. No matter who you are or what you've done, the Almighty has offered a free gift of salvation for you—a way out of your sin.

Heed His Word and remember its promise—both good and bad.

"He tells us in First Corinthians chapter ten, verse thirteen: 'No temptation has overtaken you except such as is common to man; but God is faithful who will not let you be tempted beyond what you are able, but with the temptation will also make the way of escape, that you may be able to bear it.'

"He also tells believers that we must walk through the temptations. Even the great apostle Paul declared that he battled against his flesh, that he did things the Spirit of God did not want him to do, and didn't do things the Spirit wanted him to do. Do any of us think we're greater than Paul, or even close to duplicating the purity of our Savior?"

"No, sir," Nicholas offered. Heads shook in the negative.

"Right," Francis said. "Even believers struggle. But Paul writes in Ephesians chapter four, 'You were taught, with regard to your former way of life, to put off your old self, which is being corrupted by its deceitful desires; to be made new in the attitude of your minds; and to put on the new self, created to be like God in true righteousness and holiness.'

"Remember, 'if anyone is in Christ, he is a new creation. The old has gone and the new has come.'"

Francis looked about in the audience for Harvey Smith and found him planted lovingly beside his wife, Grace.

"We in this building know firsthand the power of God to change us. And we've heard James chapter one, verse twenty-one, which tells us to 'get rid of all moral filth and the evil that is so prevalent, and humbly accept the word planted in you, which can save you.'

"So, I ask, *can* any of us plagued by intemperance overcome it?"

"Yes," came the response from the congregation.

"*Must* we overcome it?"

"Yes!" resounded the answer.

"Remember, the first effect of sin is to make us a slave. So you are either slaves to God, or slaves to sin. Whomever you obey, that is the one to whom you are slaves. It's your choice. But, remember, dear friends, 'the wages of sin is death, but the gift of God is eternal life in Christ Jesus our Lord.' *That* is a gift!"

Francis stepped to the side of the pulpit. "So, what will you have? The harsh and bitter consequences of sin and the danger of living immorally and thoughtless of God? Or the blessings flowing from our heavenly Father?

"Yet, don't love the Lord for what He says, but for who He is."

•••••

After the service, Robert and Deborah Matthews invited Francis, Nicholas and the Bracketts to late-night tea. Francis and Nicholas accepted, while Sam and Abigail begged off to get young Thomas to bed, for it was late. Several men had come forward after the sermon, seeking deliverance from demon liquor. Francis, Nicholas and the pastor laid hands on them, and they were sent away walking a foot off the floor.

At the Matthews home, Robert led Francis and Nicholas to the parlor, while Deborah busied herself at the fireplace, hanging a kettle of water over the flames.

After sitting down, Robert said, "I've always wanted to know, Francis, what you thought to be the most important contributing factor to success of the Methodist efforts in America."

"Besides God, you mean?" Francis smiled.

"Why, of course."

Nicholas put in, "Why, Bishop, that would be your decision to stay in America when all others returned to Europe at the start of the Revolution."

"I have another," Francis said, rubbing his chin. "Besides God, that is."

"What would that be?" Deborah asked. She had arrived with a plate of cookies, a tea cozy and four tea cups atop a tray.

"Our letter congratulating General Washington on his election as our first President. We Methodists were the first to do so, and that has held us in good stead ever since. It has opened doors to speak at state legislatures as well as to Congress. Who knows that we would be as welcome in the houses of the governors and judges and doctors and industrialists and businessmen and other great men of the day, had we not done so. Governor Van Cortlandt in New York is a good friend. Why, Governor Tiffin in Ohio even built a Methodist chapel. The letter to President Washington was written about in newspapers across the country, making headlines in Mister Franklin's *Pennsylvania Gazette*, his brother James' *New England Courant* and other colonial newspapers."

It was a day Francis would never forget. The Methodist Episcopal Church's annual Conference met in New York City, approved his drafting the letter, and a meeting was set with Washington, who happened to be there for his inauguration. Standing before the American hero, Francis read:

> We're conscious, from the signal proofs you have already given, that you are a friend of mankind; and under this established idea, we place our full confidence in your wisdom and integrity for the preservation of those civil and religious liberties which have been transmitted to us by the providence of God and the glorious Revolution, as we believe ought to be reposed in man.
>
> We have received the most grateful satisfaction from the humble and entire dependence on the great Governor of the universe which you have repeatedly expressed, acknowledging Him as the source of every blessing, and particularly of the most excellent Constitution of these States—this Constitution, which is at present the admiration of the world, and may in the future become its great example for imitation. Therefore we enjoy a holy expectation that you will always prove a faithful and impartial patron of genuine, vital religion, the grand end of our creation and present probationary existence.
>
> And we promise you our fervent prayers to

> the throne of grace, that God Almighty may endue
> you with all the graces and gifts of His Holy Spirit,
> that He may enable you to fill up your important
> station to His glory, the good of His Church, the
> happiness and prosperity of the United States, and
> the welfare of mankind.

Washington rose, bowed to Francis and calmly but earnestly read his reply:

> It shall be my endeavor to manifest the purity
> of my inclinations for promoting the happiness of
> mankind, as well as the sincerity of my desires to
> contribute whatever may be in my power toward
> the civil and religious liberties of the American
> people. In pursuing this line of conduct, I hope, by
> the assistance of Divine Providence, not altogether
> to disappoint the confidence which you have been
> pleased to rest in me.

> It always affords me satisfaction when I find
> agreement in sentiment and practice between all
> conscientious men, in acknowledging homage to
> the great Governor of the universe, and professing
> support to a just civil government.

> I trust the people of every denomination, who
> demean themselves as good citizens, will have
> occasion to be convinced that I shall always strive
> to prove a faithful and impartial patron of genuine,
> vital religion. I must assure you, in particular, that
> I take the kindest part the promise you make of
> presenting your prayers at the throne of grace
> for me, and that I likewise implore the Divine
> benediction on yourselves and your religious
> community.

Francis, thinking of that moment, shook his head in sadness at the thought of this great man's death. "Matchless man!" he said. "At all times he acknowledged the providence of God and never was he ashamed of his Redeemer. I believe he died not fearing death."

Robert, Deborah and Nicholas all agreed.

"Listen, I mention the importance of the nation's leaders only because they can so powerfully affect all our lives," Francis said. "We must take heed that party and politics do not drive out all our piety; they don't mingle well. And the time is coming when all kings and rulers must acknowledge the reign of the King of kings, or feel the rod of the Son of God. Foolish people think they have a right to govern themselves as they please."

"That's right," Robert said.

"Aye, and Satan will help them! Will this do for us? Is not this republic, this land, this people, the Lord's?"

"Yes," Nicholas said. "We acknowledge no king but the eternal King."

"Correct," Francis said. "And if our great men will not rule in righteousness, but forget God and Christ, what will be the consequence? Ruin!"

"*Ruin* is correct," Robert said. "And so often I fear for the flock up here. I so often fail to impart fire into their lives!"

"That's not your worry," Francis said. "That's God's job. Yours is to speak forth His Word."

"But I've seen the power of God move in revivals and your camp meetings, and I want to see that here," Robert said.

"Ah, there you have another powerful way God has moved this new race of Americans forward toward heaven!"

"I've never been to either one—revival or a camp meeting," Deborah said, pouring tea for everyone. "Tell me about them."

Francis recalled that first series of revivals. It happened in 1787 in Brunswick, Virginia, moving from Mabry's Chapel to Jones' Chapel in Sussex.

This was a very uproarious gathering. Francis and a score of other preachers had been praying fervently in a nearby home, asking God to move powerfully among the people, to show Himself great and awesome. Then they set out for Mabry's Chapel. But even before they arrived, hundreds of believers who had already reached the chapel began to weep and shout. Many trembled so violently at the mere sight of the temple that their hats were shaken from their heads. Many could not enter the building, as if held back by an unseen force; and so they walked in the woods, screaming, either in torment or in glory.

Francis heard the noise from a quarter-mile away, and when he and his colleagues arrived, the whole congregation was on its collective knees.

Without a word spoken, scores began to faint, fall over, or have fits. Some were lying about and struggling as if they were in the agonies of death.

Outside the chapel, Francis told his protégés, "Go among them. Preach, pray and exhort them, gentlemen."

Stepping inside the chapel, he shouted, "The Holy Spirit is present!" He looked about and saw black and white, rich and poor, together. Even the rich rolled on the ground in their fine silks and broadcloths, groveling on the floor and crying their fear of the loving God. "And He is no respecter of persons!"

The din was so loud that he doubted he could be heard beyond a few yards in the distance.

Hundreds were so overcome by the power of God that they fell down and lay helpless until evening.

Another day, at Jones' Hole Church, groans and shrieks rose from all parts of the church and surrounding woods as sinners struggled against the power of the Holy Spirit. Some held unconscious friends in their arms. Others crawled about, wailing in conviction. Dozens of others stretched on the floor as stiff as so many sticks.

There were fits and convulsions, twitchings and blood-curdling shrieks.

Francis and his colleagues walked among the people, ministering in whatever way they could. Then he heard two men quarreling above the noise.

Stepping closer, he found that they were two well-known aristocrats and they were arguing about who would precede whom through the gates of paradise!

"Gentlemen!" he interrupted. "Remember, the first shall be

last and the last, first!"

That stopped the dispute.

A few moments later, Francis heard a strange and very loud creaking. He bent his head, lifting an ear intensely to make out the sound. The hair on his back suddenly stood up.

"Out!" he hollered. "Everybody get out of the church!" He rushed into the crowd, pushing people out the door, lifting them off the floor. "Get out quickly!"

The creaks in the beams of the church grew louder and Francis noticed the side wall nearest him, about six feet away, begin to sway, like a person rotating his hips. With a last shove to a heavy-set woman whom he had just lifted off the floor, Francis dived with her toward the front doorway. Crash! came the wall down behind them. The wall landed no more than a yard away from Francis' prone feet with a thundering "thud!" and sent dust flying into the air.

Coughing and sputtering, Francis and the lady sat up and looked around them. Everyone had apparently escaped from inside the church. Outside, it was as if nothing odd had happened at all. The wall's collapse merely brought on fresh outbursts of frenzy.

"It's an awesome sign of the presence of God!" one of Francis' preachers cried out.

One man entered the demolished church and pranced through it, screaming, "God hit me! God hit me with a brick!"

Learn your lesson, then, Francis thought. *If you can take pride at personally being hit by a brick by God, you may take pride in anything.*

•••••

Francis recalled one of the early Western Conferences. The needs of his itinerant preachers were distressing.

"Bishop," said one, "I've no coat. The one I had was so full of patches, nothing was left of the original!"

Francis removed his long coat and handed it to the poor fellow.

The meeting was about over, and he couldn't have one of his own wandering the woods coatless.

Minutes later, another young man, whom Francis had sent to preach a circuit along the Ohio River Valley, approached.

"Bishop," he said, "this is my last shirt." He opened his overcoat to point out a tattered shirt beneath. "I have no second shirt to substitute."

Francis took off his shirt and gave it to the fellow, then approached his horse and removed a shirt from the saddlebag. As he was buttoning it, yet another young preacher stepped up to him. His head was bowed in humility. "Bishop, pray for me. I'm lacking faith."

"Why do you say that, son?"

"You see the clothes I wear?"

Francis nodded.

"They're the same ones I was wearing when I started my circuit a year ago. They're threadbare, as you can see, and I've prayed for new ones. But to no effect. Will you pray with me for more faith?"

Francis unbuttoned the few buttons he had buttoned, removed the shirt and gave it to the young man. "Your prayers are answered this day, Carl."

"Thank you, sir!" he replied and immediately changed shirts, removing his old one and putting on Francis' shirt.

As Francis stood bare-chested, a Christian friend came around behind Star, Francis' horse at the time.

"Bishop," he said.

Startled, Francis spun about to see a man he had known almost since arriving in Philadelphia. He regularly attended church and fellowship meetings in Philadelphia, and had recently moved his family west.

"Hello, Paul!" Francis extended his hand. "I thought I saw you at the back of the room when I was preaching earlier."

"Well, you know, I wouldn't miss your preachin', Bishop." Paul hesitated. Francis sensed something was on his friend's mind.

"What is it, Paul? What can I do for you?"

Paul looked gingerly at Francis' condition, being without coat or shirt. He was probably rethinking his request, but, in the end, pushed ahead anyway.

"I hate to ask this, Bishop. But can you lend me fifty pounds?"

Flabbergasted, Francis looked at his friend. "You might as well ask me for Peru!

"Dear friend," Francis added, "this is all the money I have in the world." He removed twelve dollars from his pocket. "Here's five."

The most Francis ever earned was eighty-nine dollars a year, and a good portion of that he sent home to his mother, who had become a widow. Sometimes, too, he gave his money to his circuit riders.

•••••

Using some of the rest of his money, Francis bought a shirt and coat in a nearby general store. Then he and several other preachers rode off. As evening descended, they arrived at a simple log-cabin tavern between Crab Orchard and Powel's Valley, Kentucky. Francis, his black coat pulled tight about him, entered the door first. Smoke from the fireplace and men's pipes filled the air, along with the smell of whiskey and rum.

When the door opened, all eyes fell on Francis and his comrades.

"Preachers!" hollered one man sitting at a card table, following with a litany of swear words.

"Ha!" said a companion. "Come to feed us lies, eh?!"

"No room at the inn!" called a third, slapping his cards down on the table and laughing hysterically at his own joke. "Get it? Ha! No room at the inn!"

Guffaws and oaths fell upon the ears of the party of preachers.

Francis looked grimly at the group. Wild mountain men,

hunters, a rough crowd indeed. A test!

He was about to speak when a man wearing an apron, obviously the innkeeper, approached. Scruffly dressed himself, he nonetheless bowed slightly to Francis. "Follow me, sirs. There's another room you'll find more to your liking."

He led them through the crowd of jeers to a back room. Once in the room, he turned to Francis and the others. "Can I get my wife to cook you up some dinner?"

Francis nodded. "That'd be appreciated, sir. We're cold, tired and hungry."

"All heading somewhere?"

"All leaving somewhere," Francis replied. "A Methodist conference."

"Aha!"

The man left the room and Francis and the others hung up their coats and made themselves at home on simple, straight-back wooden chairs around a long oval table.

A moment later the door opened and in walked one of the carousers from the other room. When he spoke, Francis recognized the Bristol accent. He sauntered in. "You're Bishop Asbury, aren't you?" he asked, looking directly at Francis.

Francis rose from his seat. "Yes. And you?"

"Alister Figg."

"Related to the boxing champion?"

"Not that I know." His eyes flashed. "But I have clocked a few heads in my time."

"I'll bet." Francis said it without a smile.

"But I'm not interested in clocking heads now."

"Good."

"I'm interested in some questions of religion, sir."

"Such as?"

"Is there really a heaven and a hell?"

"Yes and yes."

"How do ya know?"

"The Bible tells me so."

"How do ya know the Bible's true?"

"Point out one other book that correctly foretells hundreds, yes, thousands, of events—and they've all come true. No, sir, point out one book that foretells just one event that's come true."

Figg thought for several seconds, then shook his head. "I rightly can't do that."

"So you must accept the Bible as true."

"At least some of it."

"What part do you question?"

"Well, I daren't say."

"Daren't you?"

"Say," the man shot back, "are you making merry with me?"

Francis stepped back. "No, sir. I make merry at no man's expense, for we're all God's creatures. To make merry of you would be to make merry of the Creator."

"All right, then." Figg rubbed his chin. "Again, how can I know that when I die I won't simply be worm feed?"

"When you're burning in the firey furnace of hell, that should just about convince you," Francis replied. "Mister Figg, may I ask you, have you been seeking religion?"

"Oh, yes, for a long time. But I've not found it yet. I have succeeded in one thing: a Baptist preacher has broken me off from swearing profanely."

"Ah," Francis said. "Well, keep on reforming and you may come out a good man at last."

"So, you don't think me a good man now?"

"I won't judge that. I can't say."

"Can't say or won't say?"

"If I can't I won't."

"You're a jumble of words, Mister Asbury."

"You're a jumble of contradictions, Mister Figg."

"How's that?"

"You say you've been seeking religion for a long time. But Jesus says, 'Open the door to Me and I will come and sup with you.' Apparently, you haven't truly asked if you haven't found."

"Well, I certainly haven't found any answers from you, sir. I've heard great and swelling words about your preachin' and how your words can move men to faint and how you're more famous than President Washington. I see none of that before me." At that, Figg turned on his heel and left the room, swinging the door shut with a bang behind him.

As Francis and his colleagues dined a few minutes later, they heard the Englishman swearing and cursing loudly in the other room.

After a half hour of this, Francis opened the door and walked straight through the crowd to Figg.

Figg followed the startled eyes of a companion and saw Francis approach.

"Sir, you're from Bristol, are you not?" Francis asked. "And were you an iron smelter there?"

"How'd you know, and so what if I was?"

"Then you ought to know that two opposites can not be melted together."

Figg nodded. "So?"

"Truth—that is, God—can not mingle with lies—that is, Satan," Francis said.

"Right."

"You told me a certain Baptist preacher had broken you off from swearing, but I find you can both lie and swear. You, Mister Figg, are a son of the father of lies. Of course you've not found religion. If it stood up and gave you a roundhouse that knocked you to the ground for a count of ten, you wouldn't find it!"

At this, the Englishman approached him with fire in his eyes, his fists balled tightly, and hissed through his teeth, "I beg your pardon, Bishop Asbury."

Not backing off an inch, Francis said: "Ask pardon of God, whose Name you've blasphemed. Repent of your sins, and do so speedily, or iniquity will prove your ruin."

At this reproof, Figg was mum and turned away from Francis. Francis returned to the back room. No jeers accompanied him, and several minutes later the entire company of party-goers left the house to quietness and the preachers.

Francis and the other preachers slept in the inn that night and the next morning the innkeeper told them to beware. "There are reckless criminals among last night's crowd," he said. "Some are known for laying aside their hunting dress, painting themselves and dressing as Indians. Then they lie in wait and intercept the travelers, robbing them and often murdering them as well."

"Ha!" Francis said. "They'd find robbing a group of preachers fruitless. We own what we wear upon our bodies and little else! Besides, the Lord's angels watch over us. But thank you for the warning, friend. It's a good deed on your behalf and I'm sure the Lord has taken note of it. Come judgment day, though, He'll require more of you than this gesture. Today you could meet your Maker, and I can see from your present condition that you'll be found wanting. Are you ready to repent, dear sir?"

Standing in the doorway, the innkeeper was taken aback. "Why—why, yes, I guess so."

"Guesses and estimates, and maybes and 'I-thinks' count for nothing in the sight of God, friend," Francis said. "Again, are you ready to repent?"

This time, the innkeeper's shoulders straightened and he nodded firmly. "Yes, Bishop, I am."

There, before the preachers and the woods, the innkeeper made acquaintance with his God.

As they rode off, Francis turned to the young man closest him and said, "Some days I feel that I'm in a furnace. May I come out purified as gold."

•••••

Francis looked up from his recollection to see Nicholas, Robert and Deborah before him.

"I'll wager you have a million of those stories," Robert said.

"Oh, some of the best are about our camp meetings," Francis said, "and you mentioned you'd been to one or more."

"Certainly did. With members of the Rehoboth congregation in Lincoln County, North Carolina," Robert said. "And another at Shepherd's Crossroad in Iredell County."

"What's so memorable?" asked Deborah.

"Women and children joined in, not just the men so common in Baptist camp meetings," Robert said. "And there were Presbyterian ministers as well as Methodist. All together. All worshiping God. All camped out under the stars, in pockets of tens through the woods. Settlers came from a hundred miles away, bringing bedding, food and tents, or a covered wagon to sleep in. Fires blazed here and there in the night, casting out the darkness.

"It was much like Bishop Asbury just told of the revival, but these went on for a week or more. One day there was preaching for fourteen hours. People were saved and delivered. Demons were cast out of people, screaming their way to hell.

"The camp meeting in Rehoboth was organized by your nephew, Daniel, I believe, Bishop."

Francis nodded agreement. He had seen his nephew a couple of times and his was an incredible salvation story.

"There was preaching each morning, afternoon and evening, and sometimes the crowds became so frenzied that it continued deep into the night, depending first on the light of the moon and stars, and then of torches that flickered through the trees of the forest.

"There were times of rejoicing in my own heart. I've never felt the presence of God more strongly."

"I pray to God," Francis said, "that there may be a score of camp meetings every week and wonderful seasons of the Lord in all directions."

"Scores a week?!" Nicholas said. "Where would we go?"

"Where wouldn't we go?" Francis said. "Imagine it, son. Already, there are four or five hundred planned this year. I remember one I organized outside New York City where six thousand attended. Oh, and one near Nashville, Tennessee.

"Nicholas, Robert, Deborah," he said, looking them all in the eye, "you'd have been in heaven there! The meeting place was in the open air, in the bosom of a wood of lofty beech trees. Methodists and Presbyterians, united in their labors, mingled with the childlike simplicity of the primitive times. As fires raised light toward the heavens, shouts of redeemed captives split the night air, and cries of precious souls struggling into life, real life, broke the silence of midnight.

"The weather was delightful, as if heaven smiled down upon us while God's mercy flowed in streams of salvation to perishing sinners."

"What's the key ingredient for these moves of God to work, Francis," Deborah asked.

"A church without evidence of the influence and experience of the operation of the Holy Ghost is dead," Francis said. "And whatever may be its forms, or however sound its confession of faith, it has no more title to be reckoned a Christian church than a statue or corpse to be esteemed a living man."

Murmurs of agreement met this declaration.

"The form in which the church appeared in the best, the primitive age, under the immediate inspection of the apostles and disciples of the Lord, deserves our consideration," Francis added. "I wish to confine myself to the words of the Holy Ghost, without any regard to the traditions of men. Jerusalem was the fruitful womb from where the noble army of martyrs, confessors and evangelists went off to battle, holding up the Word of light, diffusing the blessings of the glory of God the Savior to the ends of the earth."

Francis looked at Nicholas and the Matthewses and continued. "The Lord's twelve disciples and the seventy He sent out to preach and teach were all endowed with miraculous powers. Without those powers from the Holy Ghost, the church will fail."

•••••

"Schools and colleges," Robert piped up. "They've been instrumental in training up preachers, haven't they?"

"Well, our object is not to raise ministers of the gospel, but properly to educate the sons of our patrons and friends, our married preachers, and orphans," Francis said. "And the original idea wasn't mine but that of John Dickens, who was my companion in seventeen hundred and eighty when we traveled throughout North Carolina."

"Really?" Nicholas said.

Francis laughed. "John should get more credit than I, for it was his idea. He drafted what I called 'a Kingswood School in America,' which we hoped would be a school—that's a school, not a college—for the good of thousands. I took the idea to Tom Coke for several years. Finally, he agreed, but thought it should be a college. After some debate, I agreed and, finally, we were able to raise five thousand dollars and build Cokesbury College, which opened in Abingdon, Maryland, south of Baltimore. Student enrollment: twenty-five. Faculty: three.

"By the way, the Methodist Conference chose that name, Cokesbury, not Tom nor I. They wanted to honor us. I felt the honor went to God. And I look forward to the streams that will flow from the fountains of sanctified learning that we now have in all these schools around the country, from Bethel Academy in Kentucky to Ebenezer Academy in Brunswick County, Virginia, and Uniontown in Western Pennsylvania."

"Well, you've certainly reached the thousands," Deborah said.

"Yes, and it could be more, but we've had to be selective," Francis said. "Primarily, we don't admit students indiscriminately in any of our schools because the admission of all sorts of youth into a seminary of learning is pregnant with bad consequences. Nor are the students likely to retain much religion in a school where all who apply are admitted, no matter how corrupted they might be in principle as well as in practice. All too frequently, the parents themselves have no more religion than their offspring!"

Francis sat back and sipped his tea.

"Here, it's going cold," said Deborah. "Let me top if off to heat it up. She went about adding tea to everyone's cup.

"Thank you, dear," Francis said, taking hold of his cup. "You know, the same way your cup cools off unless you keep filling it with hot tea, so does the Holy Spirit cool off in you if you stop filling yourself with Him. That is a key to a Christian education just as it's a key to Christian living. Always seek God. That's why it's so important for preachers to follow Mister Wesley's doctrine for them, spending hours every day in reading the Bible and hours more in prayer. Without it, we perish. Or, at least, our ministries are to no effect.

•••••

Francis took a deep breath, reflecting on the memory of opening Cokesbury.

Robert broke the silence. "Do you have any regrets?"

Francis thought a moment, then replied, "That, after I set sail from England in seventeen hundred seventy-one, I never saw my dear father or mother again." Tears welled up in Francis' eyes. "My father died in seventeen ninety-six and I've felt the orphan ever since. He allowed the gospel to be preached in his house for thirty-seven years. And my mother—what a very dear woman. I sent her money all these years until her death just seven years ago at the age of eighty-eight. But it wasn't the same as sending myself.

"She lived a woman of the world until the death of her first and only daughter, my older sister Sarah, when I was a child. How she would weep and tell of the beauties and excellencies of her lost and lovely child, pondering on the past in the silent suffering of hopeless grief! But God turned the evil meant by Satan to good, leading her out of her grief to Him. When she saw herself a lost and wretched sinner, she sought religious people. For fifty years her hands, her house and her heart were open to receive the people of God and the ministers of Christ. And thus a lamp was lighted in a dark place called Great Barr, in Great Britain.

"My mother was refined, modest and blameless. She wept with those who wept and rejoiced with those who rejoiced. Few have done more by a holy walk to live and, by personal labor, to support the gospel, and to wash the saints' feet. As a friend she was generous, true and constant. As a mother she was unparalleled."

Francis wavered, then added. "She died in eighteen two."

Taking a handkerchief to wipe a tear from his eye, Francis went on. "And I regret not being there with John Wesley at his deathbed. What greater and more noble man ever lived?

"It was his doctrine of free and universal grace and sanctification that led me to the Savior. It was his teaching and his writing, like his *Explanatory Notes upon the New Testament*, that inspired me. And it was John's call to America that I heeded.

"Regrets? That my attempts to end slavery have, so far, failed. I pray it will be abolished—and soon— before it destroys more souls, slave and slave-holder alike.

" I wish my preaching could have penetrated more hard hearts. The sailors on the trip here, for instance. If you were a sailor, daily dealing with possible death, wouldn't you want to know God and know that angels protect you?"

Francis looked at Robert. "You could ask the same question of Jesus." Francis looked up, as if looking at a person standing before him, and said, "Lord and Savior, do You regret not traveling the world with Your message?'

"Our Savior Himself never personally spread the New Covenant beyond the country in which He was born, except on one or two visits across the border. But He did His part, dying the perfect sacrifice for our sins. And look how the message has been spread—by countless thousands throughout the world!

"No, I believe we accomplish the little God plans for us. Our parish might be our home, our family, our village. Or our parish might be a continent. I say, be happy with the job God gives you."

Francis began to rise and Robert took the cue. "You've certainly given me plenty to feed upon, Bishop."

"And we'll certainly miss you once you leave us all tomorrow morning," Deborah said. "Next time you're here, please feel free to stay with us. And you, too, Nicholas. It's been such a pleasure to meet you."

Nicholas smiled and returned the compliment.

Francis took Deborah's hand, kissing it. "Dear lady, if the

Bracketts will not object, we would love to spend time with you as well."

Robert saw Francis and Nicholas to the door.

"I'll ride north with you and the group of men who have volunteered to be your protectors for the trip to the Conference in the morning," he said. "I'm looking forward to the experience. I still remember the three thousand men and women who tried to cram into Sewall Prescott's meeting house in eighteen hundred two."

Francis laughed. "That was a sight. Richard Whatcoat was the president then, and I'm sure many came to hear him speak. Probably they'll do the same this year. We're ordaining twenty-one deacons and seven elders as well as adding seventeen preachers—a small increase and fair prospects for the future."

"God blesses hard work," Robert said.

"And a town, Monmouth, that supports one of the strongest churches in New England," Francis said. "That one town has produced more than a dozen ministers and local preachers."

"God's will, we'll do the same here. Keep me in your prayers, will you, Bishop? And I'll keep you in mine."

"I will," Francis said. "And I appreciate your doing so as well. You're doing a fine job here, Robert. As much as I don't like my preachers setting down roots, I think you can handle this circuit from your home here. Jesse Lee can take care of the rest."

"Sure will."

As Asbury and Nicholas walked away, Robert was left thinking how he would miss Francis' preaching, and that he had certainly gained from it. Was Francis an extraordinary preacher? His preaching was characterized by a mind under control of the Holy Spirit, a heart filled with spiritual passion and a life driven by the Word—all combined to flow into speech as molten steel is poured into holy, unblemished forms.

Indeed, speaking with the authority of an ambassador of God and with credentials bearing the seal of heaven, Francis seemed to put the shofar to his lips and have the Almighty blow the message. And it was a trumpet blast declaring God the Anointed One, God the Judge, God the Summoner, God the Lover.

Listeners trembled, and their hearts were changed. That was the essential result, the bottom line, Robert thought.

CHAPTER 12

Wolf-Pack Attack

The next morning, Francis was reading by candlelight when the household woke up.

"I don't know how you do it, Francis," Sam said, shaking his head in disbelief when he reached the bottom of the stairs. *It must have been midnight when Francis and Nicholas returned last night*, he thought. *How long has he been up? How long did he sleep?* "Are you reading anything special?"

"I find that the more I seek the Lord and know Him, the less I desire of the world, to seek and to know the world," Francis said. "The treasure in this Book continues to expand for me each and every day. To think, we all can commune with the Creator of heaven and earth—and we choose not to!"

"Sad, isn't it?" Abigail asked as she descended the stairs behind Sam.

"So sad," Francis said, "that sometimes in the midst of laughter, I catch myself short. I think, 'How dare I laugh when sinners are dying? Has joviality a place—until all know, and bow their knee to their Lord and Savior?'"

"But then there would be no laughter until Christ comes to earth again," said Nicholas, who had entered the room.

"True enough," Francis said. "And, besides, how could we not laugh at the sight of such a one as little Thomas?" He had spotted Thomas bumbling down the stairs, his hair all sticking up and in knots and his shirt mis-buttoned.

"Am I funny, Bishop?" Thomas asked after jumping down over the last three steps to the floor below.

"Funny in a good way, young Master Brackett," he replied.

"I was thinkin' about preachin' someday. I wonder if people would listen better if I joked with 'em."

"Well, the topic of God is a serious one, Thomas. It's not to be joked about. Men's souls weigh in the balance."

"Yep, I know. But mightn't people listen more closely if I get their attention with a good joke?"

"If that's the only way to get their attention, then maybe their attention's not worth getting."

Thomas' brow furrowed and he chewed on his lip as he reflected on this answer.

"While you're chewing on that food for thought, Thomas, who's ready for some food for the belly?" Abigail asked.

While she prepared breakfast, Thomas came to sit again on Francis' lap.

"I'm gonna keep thinkin', Bishop."

"Of what?"

"Of what you said about countin' the cost and hearin' from God to know if I'm called to follow after you."

"Here's another bit of advice, Thomas. If you want to hear from the Lord, get rid of the noise, all the things that clutter up your life; then get alone with Him and pay attention to listen more than you talk. After all, you don't know anything that He doesn't. So sit and think on His Word, and listen."

"Yessir."

"You know, Thomas," Francis patted him on the head, "the next time I return you'll be too big to sit on this old lap of mine."

"No, sir. Don't take that long!" Thomas protested.

"Son, Nicholas and I are leaving this morning. We're traveling up north for the New England Methodist Conference in Monmouth, which has become the cradle of Methodism in the region. It's the second conference we've held at that wonderful 'Old Fort' of theirs. We'll stay with Reverend Caleb Fogg; visit with Jesse Lee, who has been like a son to me, and with Philip Wagner and many others; and generally see what God is doing in this region.

"Then, after the Conference, we're embarking on a one thousand five hundred-mile trip."

"One thousand five hundred!"

"Yes," Nicholas said. "That's the distance from here to Bath, Virginia, where we'll rest for a few days before heading on to Charleston, South Carolina for the winter."

"Bath? Do you take baths there?"

Everyone laughed.

"Well, yes, they do," Nicholas said. "But I think that's not where the name came from. Perhaps Bath, England. We're going there for their hot springs."

"Hot springs! You mean the water's hot?" Thomas' eyes widened.

Nicholas nodded and smiled.

"Really, Bishop?" Thomas turned to Francis.

"It's true. That's my favorite retreat."

"That must feel g-o-o-d! Can I come?"

Francis nodded toward Sam. "I'm afraid you'd have to ask your Dad that, young man."

Sam laughed. "Grace your mother and me with another ten years of your presence before asking that question, okay, Son?"

Ten years seemed an awful distance away, but Thomas thought on it a moment and, at last, bobbed his head in agreement. "Okay, Father."

"But on our way," Francis said, "we'll be stopping here and there to see how the brethren are doing. First of all, we'll stay in Lynn, Massachusetts, a few days."

"We trekked past Lynn when we moved here!" Abigail said. "I almost made Sam stop and settle there."

"It's the perfection of beauty," Francis said, "situated on a plain under a ridge of craggy hills and open to the sea. The Methodist Society there is strong and promising. I believe that there we'll make a firm stand, and from this central point the light of truth will radiate through the state. Why, in one year we had a growth of three thousand members. One of my favorite spiritual sons,

Daniel Filler, grew up there until I sent him to minister in Halifax, Nova Scotia."

As Abigail served up scrambled eggs, sausage and biscuits, everyone sat around the table. Sam said grace and they ate heartily.

"Several of the men and I got together after service last night," Sam said. "We're going to accompany you and Nicholas to Lynn. We don't want those highwaymen to give you any trouble."

"That's very much appreciated," Francis said. "Are you sure you can leave the fields that long?"

"I'm caught up and ahead," Sam replied. "And Abigail has given us her blessing."

Francis looked at Abigail and she smiled back. "The people here in the village look after one another," she said. "Thomas and I will be fine, won't we, Thomas?"

"Sure, Mom. If I can't go with the bishop." Thomas' lips curled in sorrow.

"Bishop?" Thomas looked up at Francis. "You never did tell me the very first story I asked about."

"What was that, Thomas?"

"About the wolf that chased you."

"Ah, that would be the Northern Wolf."

"Hm-m."

Francis took a bite of sausage and a sip of strong coffee. And remembered the night. "Well, Thomas it was actually Northern Wolves, plural. There were several of them."

"Several? How many?"

"I'd guess four or five."

"Wow!"

"Have you heard of 'three-dog nights,' Thomas?"

"No."

"It's an expression that dogsled mushers use. When they lay down to sleep on a cold night, they cuddle up to their dogs. If it's cold, one dog will do. If it's very cold two dogs will do. If it's very cold and very bitter, it's a 'three-dog night.'

"Well, I don't have sled-dogs, but I do have a horse and

sometimes two, if I've got a packhorse with me in addition to Spark. This one night when I was traveling with Daniel Hitt over the Green Mountains of Vermont. Oh, it was rugged, like the rude Clinch Mountain or the rough Allegheny. And we were riding a wagon.

"When we reached the Narrows, Daniel jumped down and led the horses. I was exhausted and must have been unattentive. And before I knew it...."

Francis was on the wagon in his memory. The two horses pulled the wagon upon a rock. Up went the wheel! The wagon turned on its side. Francis let go of the reins and grabbed for the bucket seat, holding on for dear life as the wagon tilted toward a precipice that was fifty feet above the trees and jagged rock below.

The hitch connecting horses to wagon snapped and the little bit of leverage the horses had given the wagon was lost. Suddenly Francis was tossed sideways and his feet hung over the cliff.

"Frank!"

He heard Daniel call his name but he was on the other side of the wagon and Francis couldn't see him.

"I'm here!" Francis hollered. "Don't try climbing over here, or we'll both fall!"

"I'm throwing over a rope!"

With that, a thick rope came flying over the wagon. Francis held onto the seat with one arm and reached for the rope with the other hand, but it fell just shy of him.

"I missed it!" he called.

"I'll try again," Daniel called as he hastily reeled back the rope.

The wagon creaked and the angle of Francis' body dangling over the precipice sharpened. His left shoulder and arm, holding tight to the seat, began to ache with the increased weight of his body. The rope disappeared back over the wagon and a moment later came flying overhead again. This time Francis grabbed for it and felt the tip of it slip through his fingers.

"Almost!" Francis hollered. "I touched it that time!"

Again the rope slithered away, disappearing over the wagon.

On the other side of the wagon Daniel was literally at the end of his rope. What could he do? If he told Francis he was stepping up onto the wagon, Francis would forbid him and his friend would die. So he kept silent about it, looped the rope around his arm, climbed up on a plank on the underbelly of the wagon, then let go a mighty heave of the rope as far as he could throw it, holding onto the end of it by a knot tied around his wrist. "Here it comes!" he shouted.

As if in slow motion, Francis eyed the rope as it sailed toward him. Grimacing in pain, he nevertheless pulled himself upward as best he could and reached out. Miraculously, as if with eyes of its own, the rope fell into his hand; and he had a spare three feet of it to boot!

"I've got it! I've got it!" he yelled.

He wrapped the rope several times around his arm and called, "Pull away, Daniel!"

A large and strong man, Daniel slowly pulled the one hundred fifty-pound bishop to the top of the tipped-over wagon. Once Francis reached the edge of the wagon, he put one leg and then the other over the top, then jumped to the ground.

The wagon hung there, wiggling a bit, crippled by a broken wheel on its under-side.

Francis hugged Daniel. "You and the Good Lord saved my life, Daniel! If that rope had landed two feet farther in either direction, I wouldn't have caught it." He rubbed his sore shoulder. "And I could not have held on any longer."

Tears came down Daniel's face. But that was replaced by worry.

"It's getting dark, Frank, and we're without a wagon. We'll have to ride the horses and leave the wagon behind."

"Well, by the looks of the darkness descending, I think instead we'd better stay here tonight," Francis said. "At least here we can use the wagon as kindling and get a good fire going against this cold."

Temperatures were sinking quickly and a light snow started falling. He remembered the nudging from the Holy Spirit that made him feel uneasy about traveling this northern wilderness when winter lay nearby. Well, the Holy Spirit was right, Francis was wrong and winter had made a giant leap forward to early November.

He pulled his coat tightly about himself and he and Daniel set about yanking off a board here and another there to use for a fire.

Once the fire was going, they removed the harness from the horses and brought them close by them. Despite being frightened by the fire, the horses seemed to enjoy its warmth. Francis and Daniel sat close to the fire, warming their hands over its flames. Dinner for the horses was grain. Dinner for the men was hot tea; the food they had brought with them had fallen over the cliff.

Francis and Daniel got the horses to lie down so they could sidle next to them and share the body heat from the big beasts. At about midnight, Francis was thinking that of all the unpleasant days he had experienced in his travels, this was perhaps the worst. The fire was ebbing, the cold was deepening, the snow kept falling and was about three inches deep now.

And what was this? Francis awoke from a light sleep. What was this noise?

First he heard a howling. A wolf!

Then several howlings. Wolves!

"Daniel," he said, tapping his friend on the shoulder.

Daniel awoke with a start. "What?"

"Listen."

The howling continued.

Daniel grabbed for his long rifle.

The horses suddenly whinnied and huffed. One struggled to its feet, then the other.

A howl came from the woods, and the younger of the two horses reared in the air. Francis held his arms high above him and that calmed the horse enough for him to grab its reins. Daniel took hold of the other horse's reins and they tied them to a wheel of the overturned wagon.

Once that was done, the men turned toward the woods and fell silent, listening. The howling was unabated, the sound drawing closer. *The wolves are signaling one another*, Francis thought.

Closer still, they came.

Daniel and Francis looked to the edge of the light from the fire. The light ended about five yards from them. That was a frighteningly short distance if a wolf should appear. Out of the darkness, one did. Then another. And another. And another. And another. Five wolves stepped into the faint shadows beyond the light of the fire. Their eyes shone green. Francis could hear them pant; even see their breath puff out into the cold night air.

Was that a slurp? As if one of them was already tasting dinner of human?

Daniel had heard two "truths." One that wolves don't attack humans. The other that they attack them when they're hungry. The trick is to know when wolves are hungry.

One of the wolves took a tentative step closer, then stopped. "He must be the pack leader," Daniel said, putting the barrel of his rifle to his shoulder. "If they attack, I can take down one of 'em, but I won't be able to reload fast enough to get the others."

As he said that, the other four wolves stepped closer, just as their leader had done.

A moment later, the leader took another step into the circle of light. And a moment later, the others followed suit.

Daniel took aim on the leader.

Francis pushed himself close enough to the fire to grab two sticks of wood, each with one end that had turned to hot coal. "You take out the leader and then we'll fend them off with these."

All of a sudden, Francis recalled the story of Gideon and his army. The Lord whittled down the army from thousands to three hundred, so that He could show that against innumerable odds, He was sufficient to bring victory.

Francis looked at his companion. "Remember Gideon?"

Daniel nodded his head.

"The Bible tells us that faith is being sure of what we hope for and certain of what we do not see. Well, Daniel, faith is not necessarily knowing who *you* are, but being absolutely sure of who He is!"

"Ha!" Daniel said. "And He's our great Protector, right?"

"Yes, He will be our front and rear guard."

"Well, I'm not much afraid of what's behind us," Daniel said, nodding toward the wagon. "Perhaps He can be our double-guard in front, eh?"

Francis chuckled.

Just then, the lead wolf charged at them.

Daniel aimed and pulled the trigger. Bam! The wolf fell to the ground, dead instantly. The other wolves had begun to charge immediately after their leader. But the sound of the rifle startled them and they stopped in their tracks. Francis then started walking slowly at them with his charcoal-tipped stick held out in front of him. Daniel set down his rifle and took the second stick, following Francis' lead.

Forward the two men walked. Backward the wolves retreated. Forward they walked; backward the wolves retreated.

As they walked, Francis said, "Daniel, do you remember what the Lord told the Israelites to do on the seventh day of walking around the walls of Jericho?"

'No, sir."

"'Yell,' He said. 'Walk around the walls seven times on the seventh day and then yell and the walls will come tumbling down. Are you ready to yell?"

"Yep."

"I mean yell as in holler at the top of your lungs."

"Gotcha."

"All right. One, two, three—"

Sitting at the Brackett table, Francis laughed at the memory. "We screamed, young Thomas, so that they could hear us here in Maine!"

"Then what happened?" Thomas asked, his eyes large as eggs.

"Those Northern wolves turned and scampered out of there faster than they'd ever run before, or have ever run since. God put His fear in them."

"Wow!" Thomas said, and gulped.

"That's a great story," Sam said.

"We've got to remember God's Word, His promises and what He's done in the past—and then trust in Him to do so again—for us," Nicholas said.

"Right," Francis said. "It's the Living Word. It continues to course vibrantly through the veins of all those who seek fervently after it, rending their hearts, praising and worshiping Him and striving to 'enter in' with Him, to find refuge under His wing, to get close enough to hear His heart beat and to know what His heart beats for, to do His will and His good pleasure.

"He declares, 'Abide in Me and I will abide in you.'"

With that, Francis put a napkin to his mouth and pushed his chair back. Looking at Abigail and then Sam, he said, "We thank you, dear ones, for letting us abide with you these few days. I know it's been a strain."

"In fact," Sam said, "it's been a blessing. And a double blessing because we were able to hear your life story."

"Well, I've never told it before," Francis said. "But I'm sixty-four years old now and I feel like the apostle Paul must have felt when he wrote Timothy: *'I have fought the good fight, I have finished the race, I have kept the faith. Now there is in store for me the crown of righteousness, which the Lord, the righteous Judge, will award to me on that day—and not only to me, but also to all who have longed for His appearing.'*

"You know," Francis put his arm around Thomas' shoulders, "the sun's progression through the day is like the Lord's presence in our lives from the time of our salvation onward. The moment we're saved is so strikingly beautiful—like the sunrise. Then the sun shines throughout the day—and even when it's cloudy, we know it's there. Like the heat of the sun, we can feel the love of God. And like the sun's brightness, the Lord shines into our dark corners and His light illumines His Scriptures to us.

"And when we die and join the Lord in heaven, it's magnificent—like the sunset. I look forward to that day, but know it won't happen until He Himself wants it to happen. And I know this as surely as I stand here before you, that as surely as the Almighty sent Paul to take the Gospel to the Corinthians, the Ephesians and the Romans, He sent me to take it to America.

"And as Paul told the Philippians: 'That I may know Christ and the power of His resurrection, and the fellowship of His sufferings, being conformed to His death, if by any means, I may attain to the resurrection from the dead.

"'Not that I have already attained, or am already perfected; but I press on to that I may lay hold of that which Christ Jesus has also laid hold of me.

"Brethren, I do not count myself to have apprehended; but one thing I do, forgetting those things which are behind and reaching forward to those things which are ahead, I press toward the goal for the prize of the upward call of God in Chist Jesus.'"

"Wow! Bishop," Thomas piped up. "You know all that scripture?"

"Never think that you know it all, Thomas." Francis sighed. "Never think that you know it all."

A knock at the door drew their attention to it.

"Come on in," Sam called.

Harvey Smith stepped inside. "We're all here and ready to escort you all the way to Monmouth!" he said.

"Good! Brother Fogg will be waiting for us in Monmouth. And Brother Bradbury in New Gloucester will attend to us on the way." Francis hesitated and assessed the man before him. "You look a saved man, Harvey."

Harvey simply nodded, his face beaming.

"Bishop! Bishop!" Thomas jumped in front of Francis. "Do ya really, really hafta go?"

Francis got down on one knee and placed a hand on each shoulder. "Young Master Thomas," he said, "we may be apart in miles but we will never, ever, ever be apart in spirit. Pray for me, son, and I'll pray for you. Each and every day of the rest of my life."

A tear rolled down the boy's cheek and a matching one fell down Francis'.

"And if I don't see you back here in Scarborough, or even

on this earth again, remember, we'll have an eternity together as children of God in His heaven.

"Now, I have something for you." Rising again to his feet, Francis reached for his satchel, opened a pocket and withdrew two books. He handed one to Thomas. "Young man, you're old enough and wise enough, I think, to appreciate this book."

Thomas' eyes lit up. He looked at the cover. "*Pilgrim's Progress*! Wow! Thank you, Bishop!" He leaned toward Francis and hugged his leg.

Francis smiled. "You're more than welcome, my friend. I know you're on a journey of your own and maybe what you learn from this book will help you on your way."

Thomas looked up at him. "Where'm I goin'?"

Francis laughed and patted the boy on the head. "Closer to God, I think, son."

Francis turned to Abigail and Sam and held the other book toward them. Abigail accepted it. "Thank you, Francis."

"It's John Wesley's *Sermons*," Francis said. "I trust they'll bless you as they've blessed me over the years. It's a little worn, not a new copy like Thomas' is, and you'll notice many places where I've underlined words with my quill pen, but I think it will last you forever.

"Thank you so much for your hospitality."

Abigail stepped forward and kissed Francis on the cheek.

Epilogue

As Francis, Nicholas, Sam, Harvey, Robert and the other men rode from the town minutes later, none of them knew Bishop Francis Asbury would not return again. On March 31, 1816, at the age of seventy years, seven months and eleven days, he literally ended his labors with his life, near Fredericksburg, Virginia.

At his funeral his friends read:

> *Now I know that none of you among whom I have gone about preaching the kingdom will ever see me again. Therefore, I declare to you today that I am innocent of the blood of all men. For I have not hesitated to proclaim to you the whole will of God.*
>
> Acts 20:25-27

And,

> *"And of this gospel I was appointed a herald and an apostle and a teacher. That is why I am suffering as I am. Yet I am not ashamed, because I know Whom I have believed, and am convinced that He is able to guard what I have entrusted to Him for that day."*
>
> II Timothy 1:11-12